BEWD
1762

The Diary of Jack Nowles

NIGEL KNOWLES

*This book is dedicated to my wife Jennifer,
our daughter Natasha and son Keiran*

STAR
AND
GARTER
PUBLISHERS

18 WELCH GATE
BEWDLEY
WORCS. DY12 2AT
Tel: 01299 402343

Printed by Stargold Ltd., Kidderminster

October 1996

British Library
Cataloguing-in-Publication
Data. A Catalogue record
for this book is available.

ISBN 0.9519130.5.0.

i

STAR AND GARTER BOOKS

About The Author

Nigel Knowles was born in Worcester in 1946 and lived in Kidderminster until 1978 when he moved to Wood Green, London with his wife Jennifer, daughter Natasha and son Keiran. Nigel has pursued a number of occupations, including being a carpet weaver and a trade union education officer. He gained an Honours Degree in Politics and Certificate of Education. Nigel was five times a parliamentary candidate for the Labour party and an elected Councillor in Haringey. He remains a Councillor in Kidderminster at County and District level, and is Chairman of Wyre Forest District Council.

In 1990, Nigel was one of the Heinemann New Writers, with his comedy, "The Tailors Dummy."

Photo by Natasha Knowles

Other books by Nigel Knowles, still available from
'Star and Garter,' are:

"Those in Favour." ISBN . 0. 9519130. 0.X. Price £5.00
"Observations Inside a Bewdley Ice-Cream Parlour."
ISBN.09519130.18. Price £4.00
"Identity Crisis." ISBN.0.9519130.2.6. Price £4.00
"Lord Lucan - The Letters of Sabrina."
ISBN.0.9519130.3.4. Price £5.00
"Politics, Sex and Garlic Mushrooms."
ISBN.0.9519130.4.2. Price £4.99

Characters of "Bewdley 1762"

Jack Nowles	Diarist of Bewdley 1762
Tom Pugh	Welsh lodger at, "The Star and Garter."
David Fosbrook	Black slave from Virginia
Elizabeth Haddock	Owner of, "The Star and Garter Inn."
Molly Adams	Servant girl
Mistress Perkins	Spinster
Reverend Fygge	Priest of St. Anne's Church
Bartholemew Smout	Warehouse owner and merchant
Captain Henry Longmore	Worcestershire Militia
Richard Bibb	Printer
Samuel Skey	Banker, industrialist
Scrapper Bill	Pugilist
Jed Wilks	Pugilist
John Metcalf	Boxing Manager
Mr Temple	Time Keeper
Thomas Wooton	Virginian plantation and slave owner
Elizabeth Wooton	His niece, a resident of Trimpley
The Smiths	Charcoal burners

QUAKERS

Charity Peacock
Hanna Stockwood
Sarah Newey
Mary Willis
Catherine Smith
Martha Nunn
Goodyear Wildey
Edmond Hornblower
Nathaniel Cooper
Obadiah Clare
William Seager
James Penn
Mr Sturgess
The Havergal Family

IN ABSENTIA

King George III	Monarch
Lord Foley	Builder of streets and houses in Kidderminster
James Brindley	Canal navigator
The Black African Lady, Lucy	A phantom
John Butler	Fugitive haulier
James Cox	Fugitive haulier
Mr Blount	Grammar School teacher
Dr Peplow	Physician
Mr Fitzpatrick	A Lawyer
Judge Slater	Circuit Judge
Sargeant Bowman	Militia man
Donald Jones	A lawyer
Richard Baxter	Kidderminster Vicar

Reading List

1 BARNARD E.A.B. "A vanished palace." 1946. Cheshires Ltd. Kidderminster.

2 BOSWELL. JAMES. "Boswell's London Journal 1762-1763." Heinemann. 1950.

3 BRASSINGTON. W.S. "Historic Worcestershire." 1894. The Midland Education Company.

4 BRIGGS AND JORDAN. "Economic History of England." 1967. University Press.

5 BUND. WILLIS. "The Civil War in Worcestershire." 1905. Midland Education Company Ltd. B'ham, Leicester & Leamington.

6 BURTON. J.R. "A History of Bewdley. 1883. (out of print)

7 COOKE.A. "America." 1974. B.B.C. Publications.

8 DEFOE. DANIEL. "Moll Flanders." 1722. Wordsworth Classics. 1993.

9 FIELDING. HENRY. "Tom Jones." 1749. Wordsworth Classics. 1993.

10 FLINN. M.W. "British Population Growth 1700-1850." Macmillan Press 1970.

11 GILBERT. MARSHALL. Park & Purcell. "Bewdley in its' Golden Age." Bewdley Historical Research Group 1991.

12 HILTON. R.H. "The Decline of Serfdom in Medevil England." Macmillan Ltd. 1969.

13 HOBSON. K. & PURCELL C&A. "Bewdley's Past in Pictures," Vol 1. 1993. Bewdley Historical Research Group.

14 MACDONALD. ALEC. "Worcestershire in English History." 1943. Press Alliances Ltd. Fleet St. London. (reprint 1969 S.R. Pubs' Ltd)

15 MARSH. ARTHUR. "The Carpet Weavers of Kidderminster." 1995. Malthouse Press. Oxford.

16 MARSH. JEAN. "Bewdley a 15th Century Sanctuary town." Dragonfly Books. Bewdley 1986.

17 MORTON. A.L. "Freedom in Arms." 1975. Lawrence & Wishart.

17a MORTON. A.L. "A People's History of England." 1976. Lawrence & Wishart.

18 NASH. T. "Collections for the History of Worcestershire." 1782.

19 NOAKE. J. "Worcestershire Relics." 1877. Longman. London.

20 PARKER. A. "The King's Highway of Severn." Kidderminster Times. May 11th 1946.

21 PARKER. MRS. J.F. "Old Bewdley and its' Industries." 1946. Cheshires Ltd. Kidderminster. from Worcestershire Archaeology Society 1932.

22 POSTGATE. R. "Pocket History of the British Working Class." National Council Labour Colleges. 1964.

23 POULSON. CHARLES. "The English Rebels." Journeyman Press Ltd. 1984.

24 PRESSNELL. L.S. "Country Banking in the Industrial Revolution." 1955. Oxford.

25 SMOLLET. TOBIAS. "Humphry Clinker." 1771 Penguin Classics. 1985.

26 SNELL. LAWRENCE. "Essays towards a history of Bewdley." Wyre Forest District Council Museum Service. 1975.

27 STERNE. LAWRENCE. "A Sentimental Journey Through France and Italy." 1768. Penguin Classics 1986.

28 STERNE. LAWRENCE. "Tristram Shandy." 1760. Norton & Co. New York & London. 1980.

29 SWIFT. JONATHAN. "Gulliver's Travels" 1726. Wordsworth Classics. 1992.

30 TOMKINSON. K. & HALL. "Kidderminster since 1800." 1975. Published by the Authors, Kidderminster. Bewdley Printing Company Ltd.

31 WARDLE. PETER & QUAYLE. CEDRIC. "Ruskin and Bewdley." Published for The Guild of St. George by Brentham Press 1989.

Other Sources and References

A "THE TIMES OF BEWDLEY." 1972. Project Design. Published and printed by Powysland Newspapers Ltd. Shrewsbury. The "newspaper" gives a modern reportage account of Bewdley's past as a trading port and its' Civil War activities.

B "THE PARISH CHURCHES OF BEWDLEY AND RIBBESFORD." British Publications Company Ltd. Gloucester (reference 1310 AD) Simon de Ribbesford, first Rector.

C "A VANISHED PALACE." page 10. "Bewdley, a Royalist Garrison 14 June 1644. Charles 1st was at the House...Governor Sir Thomas Lyttleton...Tinker Fox.

D "RIBBESFORD AND OTHER POEMS." George Griffith 1859. Simpkin & Marshall. London.

E "BEWDLEY'S BURIED TREASURE." Johnson & Thomas. "Ptolemy of Alexandria, a Greek writer (A.D. 139-161) leads us to best suppose that this area of the Severn Valley was inhabited by Celtic tribes called Silures and Cornavaii from the race of Kymry." In 577 A.D. a Saxon named Caewlin ruled from Bath to Bewdley. Domesday reference to the Holy Oak. In 854 A.D. Danes destroyed the land and church of Ribbesford and Wolverley.

F "HISTORIC WORCESTERSHIRE."

P. 308. Sir Thomas Lyttleton & Sir Henry Herbert both active Royalists, were attacked by a party of horse sent by, "Fox the Tinker," from Edgbaston to Tickenhill Manor, Bewdley in May 1644 when Sir Thomas was taken prisoner.

G "A HISTORY OF BEWDLEY." "In the forest near Button Oak about 100 years ago a gold coin of the Emperor Tiberius was found."

Gii "VICTORIA COUNTY HISTORY." Bewdley reference library (describes political and military history)

H "HEREFORD AND WORCESTER COUNTY GUIDE" 1993. H.W.C.C.

There is a particular reference to, "the quayside being full of boats laden with tea, rice, cotton, sugar, and even slaves from the Caribbean." It refers also to, "The Black Boy Inn, ...a reminder of the past."

I "DR PRATTINGTON COLLECTION PAPERS." Kidderminster Reference Library.

J "WYRE FOREST DISTRICT COUNCIL OFFICIAL GUIDE." WFDC 1992. Jii "AMERICA." Accounts of slavery of black people and also white people. See page 190 and others.

K "BRITISH POPULATION GROWTH 1700-1850." Various Sources estimate the population of England and Wales for 1755 to be six million people.

L "THE DECLINE OF SERFDOM IN MEDEVIL ENGLAND." References to the Black Death 1348, Peasants Revolt 1381. The Serfs of England were held in bondage as slaves. The statute of labourers 1351 fixed wages and continued serfdom, villeinage and servile tenants. This condition of the working people related back to the Anglo Saxon period when slavery existed. There was an accepted condition of Serfdom by blood. In 1414, a Neif (a person servile by birth and by blood) in the Manor of Oddington, Gloucestershire, paid his Lord, the Archbishop of York, £6,13 sh. 4d for his freedom. In 1335, a manumission by Worcester Cathedral Priory brought in £20.

M "WALKS AROUND BEWDLEY." Bewdley Footpaths Association 1990. Stargold Printers Ltd.

N "OLD BEWDLEY AND ITS' INDUSTRIES."

"Several Inns had the 'Black Boy' for their sign. This arose from the frequent arrivals at Bewdley of foreign cargoes - sugar, raisins, dyes, spices, silk, cotton etc - mostly produced by slave labour. Often slaves were brought over as well, and kept as servants in the merchants' houses, wearing a metal collar round their necks engraved with the name of their owner."..."Skey, a chemical manufacturer, a

merchant, a gold refiner of Dowles, his private bank Bewdley Bank 1769......a cheque dated then."

O "THE ENGLISH REBELS."

There is a good and interesting account of The Monmouth Rebellion. The Protestant Duke of Monmouth, James Scott, an illegitimate son of Charles II, led an army of a few thousand against Catholic James II in 1685. The rebel army was defeated at The Battle of Sedgemoor, the rebels were tried by Judge Jeffreys at Dorchester and 1,336 were executed. "Others were reprieved and sold off as indentured labourers to work on the plantations in the West Indies. Great courtiers and noblemen competed for gifts of chained gangs of those wretched slaves who could be sold so profitably to the English sugar planters." However, those same noblemen and courtiers who had helped James II put down the Rebellion and execute the Duke of Monmouth themselves deposed James II in the Glorious Revolution of 1688. The Dutch Protestant William of Orange, the husband of Jame's daughter Mary, was invited to take the English throne.

P "THE EVELYNS IN AMERICA 1608-1805."

Printed and published by Parker & Co, Crown Yard, Oxford 1881. There were 200 copies for private circulation, edited by G.D. Skull of Philadelphia Academy & Harleian Society, London. This book gives the first hand account of a British Officer during the American War of Independence, in his letters home.

Q "COUNTRY BANKING IN THE INDUSTRIAL REVOLUTION." References to Bewdley Old Bank: local savings bank and, 252, turnpike trusts and, 374 - (as Nicholls, Baker & Crane) Christmas money, 402n; discounting at 3 per cent, 314, 320, dividends received, 263; Exchequer bills and, 422-423; stocks purchased for customers by, 261 - (as Pardoe & Co.), French Rentes and, 264.

BEWDLEY 1762

PROLOGUE

The diary of Jack Nowles emanates from manuscripts at the premises of "The Star and Garter," a 17th century lodging and drinking house, now a domestic dwelling lived in by the editor. Many of the rooms remain as at the time of the diary of 1762 including cellarage, the kitchen, sitting and bedrooms. The courtyard with its' adjacent brewing house and various out buildings is now a walled garden, but water from the surrounding high fields of Dowles and Patchet's Farm continues to perculate into the welled cellar of the old public house. Welch Gate was and is a main route out of Bewdley into the Marches area of Mid Wales. Until 1865, a Turn Pike existed just a few yards down from "The Star and Garter," putting the property, 'beyond the pale,' but offering cheaper accommodation to travellers and lodgers then properties inside Bewdley.

The Widow Elizabeth Haddock and her son are listed in Parish Records and several text books as being tax payers and occupants of, "The Star and Garter," at 18, Welch Gate, Bewdley. In 1729 her father Henry, a capper, died leaving a will of £39. 2 shillings and 10 pence. Her mother, also named Elizabeth, left £18. 6 shillings and 8 pence when she died on 24th September 1745. The good lady's husband Henry did not leave Elizabeth much on his death in 1753 - merely £4. 19 shillings and 9 pence. Therefore, the Widow Haddock seemingly had no choice but to continue keeping "The Star and Garter," as an ale and lodging house to serve the 2,628 people of Bewdley registered as paying Hearth Tax and perhaps 200 other poor souls classified as Paupers, Vagrants and Strangers.

BEWDLEY, ITS' PEOPLE AND THE RIVER SEVERN

Bewdley is dominated by the River Severn. When the Romans invaded Britain in 43 A.D. they discovered the Celtic - British had pagan gods and Sabrina was the goddess of the River Severn. This theme of pagan worship persisted as Christians established monasteries and churches along the banks of the Severn. The shallow river ford crossing at Lax Lane became the settlement of Bewdley and Wribbenhall. The Saxons occupied the area in 583 A.D., the Danes invaded in 854 A.D. destroying the land and churches of Ribbesford and Wolverley, finally the Normans arrived in 1066.

By 1446 Beaulieu, the Beautiful Place, was granted a licence for a weekly market and in 1472 Bewdley was given a Charter by King Edward IV making it a Corporation. Bewdley therefore gained a new commercial importance but the vexed issue of its' status as a Sanctuary Town was not settled because of legal disputes about County boundaries in its' Parish. Throughout this period, Bewdley was indeed a place of sanctuary for, "fugitives, scoundrels, criminals and outlaws." If such people made it to Cathems End on the outskirts of Bewdley, they considered themselves beyond the law. This freedom was related to county boundary disputes, whether Bewdley lay in Shropshire or Worcestershire, an issue not settled until 1612 by Act of Parliament. Added to this legal loop-hole was the affirmation that in living memory the west bank of the River Severn was referred to by local people as the, "Godless," side of the river. This accusatory piece of folk lore obliquely referred also to Paganism, the wildness of nearby Wyre Forest, the lawlessness of the town and the old notion of Sanctuary which set Bewdley apart.

During the Middle Ages, Bewdley was also notorious as a town occupied by river pirates. The important trade up and down the Severn from Bewdley was controlled by local watermen and bow hauliers. It was a strong brotherhood, an association of working men. Their methods were often illegal and violent. Any boat entering Bewdley was made to pay a toll as a right of passage. Petitions to Parliament from Gloucester and Bristol against the Bewdley river pirates in 1412 were not successful. Only the advent of canals and steam tug boats ended the power of the Bewdley Brotherhood. Ironically, many of these hauliers were press-ganged into the British Navy during the expansion of commerce and overseas empire. By 1571, Bewdley was the centre of a woolen cap trade which employed 1,000 people. The Statute Cap had to be worn in England, "by every person over seven years of age, on Sundays and holidays, a cap of wool knit made and dressed in England under forfeiture of three farthings---."

Bewdley became prosperous, but the 17th and 18th centuries were a turbulent period in English history. Great religious issues faced the people, Catholics were persecuted until the Relief Act of 1778 allowed them to purchase and inherit property. The English Civil War 1642-1648 had divided the country and its' people on the issue of religious freedom, the Monarchy and civil rights.

The late 18th century saw massive social change. Continued expansion of Empire and growth of foreign trade created a huge demand for English manufactured goods. Bewdley played its' part, and as early as 1677 in nearby Kidderminster 400 looms for carpet weaving were established, according to the historian Nash. The factory system was beginning to devour the peasants and agricultural labourers from the land.
The list of Bewdley trades and industries is important:
Weavers, cappers, barge makers, pewterers, trowmen, brass founders, blacksmiths, skinners, glovers, felt makers, wheelwrights, brickmakers, apothecaries, doctors of physic, barbers, tobaconnists (1700), tanneries, carpenters, hauliers, shoe makers, horn lantern makers, salt peter and chemical workers, clothiers, tailors, candle makers, bakers, butchers,

masons, grocers, hatters, maltsters, braziers, saddlers, nailers, plumbers, millers, farriers, ferrymen, brewers, gunsmiths, rope makers,gun powder production, dyers and other trades relating to agriculture and forestry.

Bewdley was a thriving centre of commerce with its' own market and fair. Warehouses covered the Quayside of the River Severn and in 1770, Nash records that stabling for 400 horses existed in Bewdley to service trade up and down the river to Bristol. It was said every other house in Bewdley was a public house and 112 are listed over the years, including two Black Boys, The Bug and Blanket, Fortunate Sweep, George III, Hole in the Wall, Labour in Vain, Mug House, Old Pack Horse, Sea Horse, Star and Garter, Wood Colliers Arms, etc.

One aspect of 17th and 18th century Bewdley trade gets little mention in any of the text books, though the two, 'Black Boy,' public houses bear testament to the vile and non-Christian slave trade. Black African slaves were brought to Bewdley Quayside from Bristol for sale into surrounding mansions of those recently enobled Lords and Ladies who owned tobacco and sugar plantations in the Americas and Caribbean, and who of course often owned slaves themselves. The trade into Bewdley was the importation of spices, cotton, tea, coffee, rice, oranges, tobacco, sugar, wine, slaves etc. Exports were woven goods, wool, pewter, coal, timber, guns, foodstuffs, manufactured goods, etc going down to Brisol.

The effect of slavery upon the people of Bewdley, indeed of England, can only be imagined. Whatever few civil rights were held by the native people of Bewdley, it is certain that the black slaves who passed through or settled in the area had none. Even a Bewdley man or woman could be hung for stealing a sheep, or deported to the colonies. Indeed, many white men and women sold themselves into slavery as debentured labourers of the plantations in the Americas, as noted by Boswell in 1763 and Alistair Cooke in his book, "America."

Life for the people in 1762 was, "nasty, brutish and short." Cholera, measles, smallpox, typhoid, even diarrhoea took the lives of Bewdley people quickly, sometimes dozens at a time in one week. During the epidemic year of 1756-57, 273 men, women and children died in Bewdley, compared to 86 in 1760.

Yet in the midst of such misery, there was happiness to. Jack Nowles knew both conditions as he lived the year of his life with Widow Haddock at, "The Star and Garter" Inn, 18, Welch Gate, Bewdley in 1762.

Nigel Knowles
"The Star and Garter"
October 1996
(The Bewdley Festival)

BEWDLEY
1762

Friday 1st January

I was utterly determined to begin the new year in a new town, so having yesterday come through Kidderminster I walked the three or four miles and crossed the river Severn last night by the old bridge and came into Bewdley. There was ice in the water and the trowmen sat huddled in their boats burning braziers which lit up their bad language for all to hear. The boatmen are notorious hereabouts and I shall try to keep clear of them particularly. I found lodgings at, "The Star and Garter" Inn, a hostelry up the Welch Gate and through a further toll gate. The keeper of the premises is the Widow Haddock and the rent is ten pence a day with breakfast and dinner.

My room overlooks the courtyard and gardens with the Brewhouse just a few yards below my window. I can smell the ale which is not unpleasant. I am writing this journal at a desk in my room and a good fire keeps me warm.

I drank heavily last night and made Merry, cavorting with wenches down from the Sandy Bank. I got to my rooms exceedingly late and toasted New Year in the arms of Molly Adams, a comely lass whose favours I did gain just as The Town Crier called out for 3 o'clock. She left my bed as it grew light, for Molly had to be at her work soon after 8.

As for me, I got up about mid day, being rudely woken by the Widow Haddock yelling at an unfortunate lodger unable to pay for his bed. I later discovered he had received the contents of the piss pot tipped over his head and his meagre belongings roughly thrown into the freezing mud of Welch Gate. 'Tis nice to know that good Christian charity remains in this blessed town of Bewdley. Indeed, it seems the good Widow must have been quite taken with the wretched man else he would surely have suffered a drenching or drowning in the Severn. By suppertime I had a vision return of my beautiful black African Lady dressed in scarlet and riding a white horse. She stopped at my door and said,

"Jack Nowles - I have come to marry you as it is written in the stars and the moons of the Heavens. Jump up on my brave stallion and let us go into the woods and forest of Wyre and be married where the foxes dance with the red, red deer. Will you come to me Jack, will you sleep with me in carpets of green, green ferns? Will you speak to me softly with a voice as soft as velvet gloves, then kiss me with sugar lips warm as the sun and hold me tightly as the roots of a tree hold the beautiful, brown good earth."

My God - I sobered up very quickly after this, but my African Lady visits me as she pleases.

Saturday 2nd January
This day was worthy of note for one reason alone - Widow Haddock has taken in a new lodger.

Sunday 3rd January
I had chops for breakfast and met the new lodger. We talked at table for a considerable time. He is a Welsh man named Thomas Pugh and has found work as a clerk in the warehouses on the Quayside.

I again walked the town and later met Thomas Pugh down by the river. My God, tis a cold forsaken place near the water, so cold. Death invites any to skip along the river bank with a few good ales within them, for once a soul slipped into the arms of the Severn goddess Sabrina, life would surely end in this world. I visited the Mug House, and was never taken by such sorely a group of men I found there. I now know they are the

Bewdley Brotherhood and that ale house is their main port of call. I felt uneasy, all eyes being on me. I was served well enough, but voices were lowered for a time until they got the jist of me, I am sure. Perhaps the men thought I was with the Revenue or even the Navy. The trouble is all about the river trade. They are jealous and fear the canal system will take away their livelihoods, I feared they would take away my life until I was joined by Thomas Pugh and he put me almost at my ease, but we left quite quickly. Sunday seems a quiet day in Bewdley with little river activity and only a few shops and ale houses open for business. St. Anne's church did enjoy a fair trade of people going in and out, including myself and Mr Pugh, though I at least am not at all of a religious mind. However, I do enjoy church buildings and the company of people and so I strike a compromise with the Lord that I will enter His house and be on my best manners, even perhaps put a penny piece into the offertory box, but on no account will I issue false and hypocritical words in His name as I think many do for reasons of social standing. I do however enjoy a good hymn and can sing with the best of those transparent Christians. Let me say I have known many true Christian people who are sincerely God fearing and gentle. It remains to be seen whether the Bewdley Congregation is mainly comprised of the former or the latter.

Monday 4th January
The Widow Haddock gave me a smile for my breakfast with fresh baked bread and cheese. She is a handsome woman, tall, with black hair and dark eyes. Her age might be perhaps thirty and she has a boy of schooling age, though whether he attends school I don't yet know. It rained hard today and is very cold, so I stayed quiet in, "The Star and Garter," writing, eating and later talking with Tom Pugh. I believe I shall venture out a little more tomorrow and perhaps not write this journal again for a day or two, allowing myself opportunity to discover more about the town and the people of Bewdley.

Thursday 7th January
Not ready yet to settle properly into my writing, but I am still alive and hearty, in spite of a few drunken roughnecks along Severn Side who tried to take my purse.

Saturday 9th January
Very well - let me now explain my recent activities in this English place where history hangs heavy and modern endeavour seems set for a hard job indeed to change the old ways. I have noticed that these country towns, unlike our old and indeed newer cities, particularly London, are filled by families which seem to have been set upon the local fields and streets ever since they arrived with the Saxons and the others. They are clannish - jealous of new comers, but they have to accept men of industry continually arriving in their midst to change society. In such a small place as Bewdley, these newcomers, or foreigners as some call them, stand out like people from the Moon. Strangers are always noticed. There are men here who have opened up Banks to keep safe the local people's money and take a handsome profit in the process. Others are pewterers and merchants, traders of new goods like sugar and cotton - these men are not local but have settled in Bewdley for commercial gain. Whereas in the cities, these occurances are treated as normal actions to be welcomed, in Bewdley there is resentment and jealous muttering about Scots or Londoners or Catholics and friends of France.

'Tis peculiar, this town, as if the people wish to be left alone, yet knowing the canals and foreign trade will pass them by and cast Bewdley adrift into a desolate, icy region of the land unless they do indeed embrace these modern changes and turn these modern perils of capitalism to their advantage.

In short, there is little or no political debate, the people are not progressive, and seem very much for the Tories, the Whigs being taken as traitors and worse. There is no debating society in Bewdley and no place for a radical. Only the minority churches - Quakers, Presbyterians, and Baptists, offer any prospect of a religion for working people, the peasantry or the dispossessed. There is no politics, no political clubs, no unions of tradesmen but the reactionary Brotherhood. However, for one such as I, prospects political and commercial seem perhaps likely. I shall address myself to these issues very soon. When I walk the streets of Bewdley I feel this to be so, because of my past life in London where I know things are changing with real speed and the old order feels similarly threatened. But in Bewdley, because it is small, of some 3,000 souls, the old order has more weight and deadening effect upon the people.

There are the Honoury Burgesses and Aldermen, numbering maybe forty men who hold sway over all matters civic and political, with their friends the Magistrates who take care of matters legal, civic, and political. 'Tis as if these fine gentlemen were ordained from on high, placed down upon the earth by an act of God, such is the reverence given up to them by the working people hereabouts. Kidderminster now is not like this, anger at the factory system in the carpet trade is stirring everyman and woman to political discontent, though nothing more yet.
The Bewdley Burgesses are powerful people indeed. It would be a coup for me to befriend one of their number and infiltrate their Rotten Borough.

Sunday 10th January
I hope to see Molly again today. We shall walk up around the woods skirting Wyre Forest, perhaps towards Cleobury or Kinlet and eat at a suitable hostelry. Molly is a good person and I am amorous towards her, though I must find out more about her before matters become complicated.

Molly's company was indeed exquisite and our day glorious in all respects. I go to my bed content and with Molly fresh in my head.

Wednesday 13th January
I have found a position with a merchant down at the Quayside. I am
until further notice therefore, a Senior Clerk with the company
Bartholemew Smout whose trade is tobacco and other goods into Bewdley
and export down river with carpet pieces from Kidderminster and many
other goods set for Bristol and the Colonies of North America.

A most interesting consideration crossed my mind whilst I was about my
duties in the warehouse - in any show of absolute power, who would win
out? The Bewdley Brotherhood of vagabonds and bruisers, or the
Honoury Burgesses? Each control a part of this town, but not the whole.
The Brotherhood controls the river, but only I think, with the unwritten
permission of the Magistrates and Burgesses. If the Brotherhood were to
properly threaten the vested interest of the towns gentlemen, we should
pretty soon see where the power lay. The Magistrates have the dragoons at
hand - who would fight for the Brothers, apart from their wives and kin-
folk? Aside from my humorous fancy of infiltrating the Burgesses, maybe
I should make the prospect a pair and infiltrate the Brotherhood whilst I
am about it? Then I should truly make the fur fly in this peculiar English
town.

Yet, for my purpose, I shall take exceeding care with what I do and say.
The awful prospect of the gibbet fills me with dread and only some weeks
ago a poor fellow from hereabouts was hung for stealing horses from a
minor aristocrat of Ludlow. It seems the rich may play the fool, gamble
their money and property, and take every advantage of their poor ser-
vants without hindrance. The poor wretch claimed not to have been paid
by Sir - and thought he would even matters up by taking away his horses
and selling them. He was arrested by the Magistrate's men and quickly
put to death before a crowd at Worcester. His trial was a farce in the best
tradition of Messrs, Defoe and Fielding, or more perhaps a tragedy of
William Shakespeare. However, 'tis a motley thing, this system of Justice.

The moral surely is - do not be caught!

Friday 15th January
Today was colder than all other of my days in Bewdley, even deep inside Mr. Smout's warehouse 'twas all I could do to prevent my teeth chattering. Fortunately our business was exceedingly quiet and we were not required to go out onto the freezing Quayside. I visited, "The George Hotel," in the evening. Traders go there and many, it appears, of Bewdley's higher society, but I was properly dressed and money breaks down most social barriers, if even for a short while.
I later talked again with Thomas Pugh in, "The Star and Garter." Our merry widow, Elizabeth Haddock, was in good form and gave us baked potatoes and mulberry wine. She smiled at me again with particular charm and mentioned Molly Adams had been sent to Worcester for a week or two by her mistress. 'Tis food for thought these women give, often beguiling when the fancy takes them, but quick to hurt, I fear, when charity goes for want of affection.

Saturday 16th January
There was a fire this afternoon in one of the adjoining warehouses which did much damage and was only put out by the heroic efforts of many men who were at hand. They formed a chain from the river and passed buckets of water to the fire for well over two hours until it was put out. Many gloves, furs and shoes, as well as the property itself, were spoiled. The business has been burned out. Mr. Smout was not on good terms with the owner, but I imagine even he would not have wished such a bad fortune upon his rival? However Smout took pity on Tom Pugh whose employment went up with the flames, and gave him work with us.

Monday 18th January
Smout's warehouse received today a large consignment of tobacco from the Carolinas, up from Bristol. Various local traders took some for sale,

7

but the majority went by pack horse to Kidderminster and Ludlow. On the trow was a remarkable man, a black slave who is the property of American plantation owners. He is called David Fosbrook and has a quiet dignity that sets him apart, even I think, from members of his own race. I brought Mr Fosbrook back to, "The Star and Garter," an action which caused the Widow Haddock a certain degree of surprise, but not so Tom Pugh who had observed me speaking with him earlier,

Tuesday 19th January
David Fosbrook shall stay here for some days. At breakfast, he began to tell Tom Pugh and myself all about his life. I say without doubt, that those men who own him and have mistreated both David and hundreds like him, must never be allowed to call themselves Christians, without challenge from me. To hear the few things said to us by David Fosbrook was sufficient to realise that evil men and women exist in the New World as in the Old.

Wednesday 20th January
Mr Fosbrook worked with me today at Smout's, unloading packages of tea, sugar and rice. Members of the Bewdley Brotherhood watched us closely from their trows on the Severnside. We paid them no heed, though Mr. Smout instructed some of their number not to inhibit our work. After our labours were finished, Thomas Pugh, David Fosbrook and I returned to, "The Star and Garter." We had the back room to ourselves and talked for hours, well into the night, not loud as to disturb the others, but with a keen sense of purpose and amazement as David told us his tale.

The issue of slavery must surely be the most Godless and awful of mankind's activities? David Fosbrook arrived in England from the town of Norfolk in the state of Virginia. Hundreds of black slaves are there, men, women and children who are born into slavery as we free-born English enjoy liberty, even if that liberty is a very meagre thing indeed for the labourers and peasants who inhabit this fair land. Though Americans have no aristocrats, they have a rich property owning class, mostly colonials from England who now enjoy the fruits of their huge plantations and the commercial profit of industry and trade.

Mr Fosbrook works on a tobacco plantation where hundreds of black people spend their lives in rude cabins and shacks. Their labour naturally is free to the plantation slave owners, something surely for the Christians to consider as they smoke their Bewdley pipes filled with rich brown Virginian tobacco? I am a young man of but twenty five years, as carefree as I may dare, with the ladies at least and by my nature also. Yet David's plight moves me most deeply and inflicts upon me a most serious mood where before there was some pleasure and gay spirit at being in my new town. David Fosbrook was born on the plantation where he yet is forced to labour. His father was sold when David was but a child, though his mother lived for many years more to raise her children as best she could under conditions of abject poverty in Slavery. Some of David's brothers and sisters were also sold to planters of indigo in the Carolinas and to Louisana for the cotton and sugar trades.

How must it be for him now, knowing his kinfolk are scattered across the land like seeds blown by a cursed wind? Redemption for Christians must surely never be given to those who own slaves? David is a Christian and believes most fervently in Redemption for all souls, even slave owners, though I told him his benevolence was misplaced and wasted on those devils in their mansions and horse drawn carriages. He said never, never had he heard a white man proclaim things thus and was startled by my boldness and that of Thomas Pugh for his steady patience and in hearing him out.
Even now, my head is filled by the words of David Fosbrook. I can not allow things to continue thus. Surely, slavery is an ungodly curse upon mankind which should be challenged and thrown over? Yet what

recourse would I have against a system so set in society? The prospect frightens me and kept me awake throughout the rest of that night. David Fosbrook slept in my room and as he did so, I looked over at him lying on a rough bed and wondered how human beings are capable of such cruelty to each other.

Thursday 21st January
We three worked hard today loading a barge for Smout at the Quayside, mostly cutlery from Birmingham, but also a good quantity of wool and Kidderminster rugs set for Bristol. David Fosbrook's gaffer has gone to Bridgnorth for a few days leaving me in charge of David, a most amusing situation given how I feel about Mr Fosbrook's condition. I find my own position as Smout's manager therefore involves a great deal more than paper work and accounts. Mr Smout himself spent much of the day in, "The George Hotel," with a good fire in the hearth no doubt and whisky in his hand to keep out the cold. David Fosbrook is a very strong man indeed and shifted as much as Tom Pugh and I achieved between us. We ate meat stew at midday then retired to, "The Saracens Head," for an ale or two before continuing our work. Several members of the Bewdley Brotherhood stood nearby as we finished loading the boat. They seemed aggressive and talked to each other yet never took their eyes from Tom Pugh, Mr Fosbrook and me. Finally, as our job was finished, they walked away, mean and huddled together like a press gang ready to pounce. I watched them go under the bridge and wished them good riddance. Mr. Smout arrived back at his warehouse just in time to bid us good evening. Perhaps I ought to start in opposition to Smout because we do the work yet he makes the real money, or so they say. Shall I therefore settle in Bewdley and open my own warehouse? I have a strange feeling that the Bewdley Brotherhood would oppose such action on my part, even though until three weeks ago, I had never visited here nor saw their ugly faces.
At around 2 hours to midnight, Mr. Fosbrook and I were drinking ale in, "The Saracen's Head," Tom Pugh having taken himself off to, "The Star and

Garter," and the charms of the Widow Haddock. One of the Bewdley Brotherhood who had watched us earlier in the day made a rough and insulting comment concerning Mr. Fosbrook. I feared trouble and trouble surely came.

"Get out of here you black devil," said the man, "for you are not welcome and I feel sick with you here."

David Fosbrook turned his back on the man and ordered two more ales from the landlord. "You dog," said the man, "to turn your back against me. Go to the river with the other black rats."

Still Mr Fosbrook looked to the landlord. "It's you I mean," roared the man, "go out blackie or I shall kick you into the street." It was then he punched David Fosbrook in the back of his head. My man shook for a moment then turned to face the Bewdley Brother whose fist was raised for another blow.

David Fosbrook drew back his shoulder and in a flash delivered a mighty blow to the man's jaw. There was no need for a second, for as David stood like a prize fighter, fists and arms up before his face, the Bewdley Brother crashed onto the floor as a fallen oak in a forest. There were gasps of astonishment from the assembly. David looked at the felled tree and threw his ale over his face, stepping over his body for the door. Thus ended the hospitality of, "The Saracen's Head," we were quickly out and away, before others pursued us.

Friday 22nd January
Mr Smout was all set to send both myself and David Fosbrook down the river to Worcester until I explained the issue from last night. I considered it a foolish thing for Mr. Fosbrook and I to make the journey, with the Brotherhood so agitated. We would not have made it a mile from Bewdley before they would have set upon us. Smout seemed unbothered by that prospect until he considered what could happen to his cargo. He hired a small gang of hauliers from Lax Lane and saw off the trow before mid day.

On this day we did not see those members of the Bewdley Brotherhood from, "The Saracen's Head" or "The Mug House," though 'tis such a small town and I wondered whether the earth had swallowed them up.

Sunday 24th January
I accompanied David Fosbrook to St. Anne's church for 10 o'clock, Tom Pugh having gone off somewhere on his own. I had dreampt again last night of my African Lady who sailed with me on a boat pulled by white horses. A common man may dream, as does a King I suspect, though perhaps it is safer for me to dream of my black lady than it would be for King George? They say he has the habit of shouting out many peculiar things in his sleep as well as in his waking time, so a dream of black ladies for George would surely make his household spin?

Monday 27th January
Mr Smout is a peculiar old fellow, secretive by nature I feel and lately as jumpy as a wild cat. He belongs to the Honourable Society of Bewdley Merchants and seems to consider that noble body of gentlemen the next best thing to Royalty. He is soon to become an Honoury Burgess of the town, due to one of their number dying on the eve of Christmas. Smout has no family and few true friends, if any, and the talk is that he is a man with a most interesting past.

I have no idea as to the whereabouts of David Fosbrook's captain who is surely some days overdue. However, Smout has instructed Tom Pugh, myself and David Fosbrook to go up into Wyre Forest with a horse and cart to seek out a family named Smith who owe Smout a load of charcoal for export down to Gloucester. We are to set off at first light tomorrow while Smout warms his behind in, "The George Hotel."

Tuesday 28th January
The dawn broke late and it was very cold. We assembled at the Quayside

*and Smout presented us with a cart and four horses. The Widow Haddock
had set us up with chops and potatoes, for I had explained to her about
our trip into the forest. She said to beware of vagabonds and cut throats
and it was with this thought in my head that we rattled past, "The Star and
Garter," on our way through Welch Gate to the forest.*

*We travelled a mile as instructed by Smout, then turned off the Turn Pike
into the forest. The horses seemed to know the track so we gave them their
head for another half an hour until we came to a clearing where a horse
was tethered near an old cottage. The Smiths were not pleased to see us,
presumably because of who we represented. They loaded the charcoal
from near their kilns and burners, without either talk or civil gesture. I
noticed in the thick woods nearby, other people came out of rude tents
erected around poles shaped as a pyramid. These poor souls must be
housed in these rough shelters. I was not sorry to be gone from there and
their cold, lonely faces are with me yet.*

*It was dark when we got back into Bewdley. After paying the Toll at Welch
Gate we went onto the Quayside where Smout was waiting in his warehouse. We led the horses into the yard and stabled them. Smout was away
quickly, but he did say that David Fosbrook's captain had sent word he
was staying in Bristol and then would leave for America. So David was
to be put in our keeping, and Smout gladly imparted our Black Gladiator
into my custody. On that note we returned to the safety of Widow
Elizabeth Haddock in whose bed I slept as soundly as a rock, after that is,
the good lady and I tripped o'er Cupid's enchanted paradise.*

Wednesday 29th January
*My breakfast was fit for a King - Messrs. Fosbrook and Pugh were all smiles
when the Widow entered the room to give me yet more bacon and tea. All
thoughts now of Cupid have gone with the night, though the good lady
remains affectionate to the point of embarrassment.*

Saturday 1st February
This town is rife with rumours that Brindley is to dig a canal here from Stafford or Birmingham. The Bewdley Brotherhood stoned a Stafford man out of town whom they suspected of being an advocate of the, "stinking ditch."

Saturday 8th February
Mr Smout has been sworn in as a Bewdley Honoury Burgess - so help him God!

Sunday 9th February
I went with Tom and David Fosbrook to St. Anne's church, yet the vicar's sermon did nothing for my spiritual well being nor did he strike a blow for religious tolerance, blaming Catholics for civil unrest and Baptists for division and blasphemy. How these Christians love to fight one another, even on the Lord's day itself, is beyond my contemplation.

Wednesday 12th February
A band of gypsy people came to town and played music at the Quayside. Their caravans were gaily painted and their horses truly beautiful creatures as well turned out and cared for as any ever I did see. The gypsies speak a strange tongue to each other when not speaking to us. They stayed over night in one of the riverside meadows then left the town towards Ludlow just as we were going down to Smouts. David Fosbrook said he liked the gypsy people and, compared to some vicars I have met, they are paragons of virtue who love their children as the Saints surely would have.

Wednesday 19th February
The Quayside was the scene of a vicious fight between the Brotherhood and men from Worcester who had been stopped at the bridge in charge of five trows bound for Bridgnorth. The cargo was confiscated and the trows

sunk. Serious trouble seems certain.

Saturday 22nd February
Trouble came in the form of twenty men on horse from Worcester city who galloped down the Quayside at mid day. The Brotherhood blocked the road off and stoned them. A huge crowd gathered to watch the fight which lasted a few minutes only before the Worcester men ran for their lives towards the forest.

Sunday 23rd February
The Burgesses keep a strong silence about yesterdays trouble and seem unlikely to send the Troopers after the Brotherhood. In any other town, the magistrates would have read the Riot Act, but in Bewdley, riots are entirely different from elsewhere - assemblies of dangerous dogs perhaps or naughty children or even unruly Maypole dancers - might engage the wrath of local magistrates, yet a violent mob turned out against "foreign" horse men does not.

Saturday 1st March
Tom Pugh wore a daffodil in his coat today, it being St. David's Day for Wales and the Celtic celebration of spring.

Saturday 8th March
Several people hereabouts have recently died of a dreadful cough and fever. Some townsfolk are to be seen walking around with cotton masks to protect themselves. Others say daily doses of gin and whisky will do the job and we three have opted for the latter. The Widow Haddock has gone to visit her sister in Kidderminster whilst Molly Adams came down to visit me. She was exceeding amorous and affectionate and I was sorry to let her return to her mistress on Sandy Bank.

Sunday 16th March

There is much activity in Bewdley just now, since a large shipment of tobacco has arrived from Virginia. Also landed was a cargo of brandy from France with African oranges, lemons and rice. The Quayside was a frantic hive of people as the boats cargoes were unloaded and put into the warehouses and onto packhorses set for out of town. We worked well into the night and Smout said we were to start at mid day on the morrow as a sign of his appreciation for our labours. That man is all heart and he must surely go to Heaven for his kind nature and fairness to his employees. Even David Fosbrook said so, though his grin indicated Mr Smout had yet a long way to travel before he reached Heaven's Gate.

Sunday 23rd March

Mr Fosbrook flattened a great lout today who had insulted him and threatened to throw him into the river. When I was in London, I saw several prize fighters slug it out for hour after hour until one of them dropped finally into oblivion. I fancy Mr Fosbrook would not detain such gentlemen for more than a minute or two.

Sunday 30th March

And so it was that yesterday I arranged for my man to fight Scrapper Bill, a local bully who stands over six feet and weighs fifteen and a half stones. The fight will take place next Saturday in the grounds of Tickenhill Palace which overlooks the town. Tom Pugh and The Widow Haddock think little of the scheme, but I am optimistic that David will be victorious.

Wednesday 2nd April

Mr Smout strongly disapproves of the fight but declines to stop it. However, if David Fosbrook is unable to work normally on the Monday following the match, both he and I will be out of his employment.

Saturday 5th April
The town is buzzing with talk of the fight. I set out a stall in Load Street to
take wagers on my man, six go on Scrapper. David Fosbrook spent the
morning lifting logs above his head and running along the Quayside.
This was my idea to gain further interest in the fight, and by mid day, I had
taken over 200 hundred guinneas for Scrapper Bill to win. If he does win
of course, David and I shall effect a good escape from Bewdley under the
cover of darkness. But David will not lose, of that I am certain.

At two o'clock, we stepped into the ring at Tickenhill in front of a crowd
of over three hundred people. I had employed a Mr. Temple to act as time
keeper and referee. He had brought a hand bell for the occasion and
after his preliminary introduction of the fighters to the crowd, the fight got
under way to tumultuous applause.

The First Round.
Scrapper Bill pursued my man around the ring yet hardly landed a blow.
For good measure and to keep the crowd sweet, Mr Fosbrook gave his
opponent a few hefty jabs to his ribs now and again. After ten minutes of
shadow boxing and sything the air with his big fists, Scrapper Bill was, I
think, glad to sit down.

The Second Round.
A repeat of the first, but David Fosbrook did more work and cut Scrapper's
lip badly.

The Third Round.
My Black Warrior punched Scrapper Bill to oblivion and back, then let
him regain his breath for the break at the end of that session.

The Fourth Round.
As he was getting up from his stool, Mr Fosbrook, or, "The Boxing Black,"

as some of the crowd were calling him, said to me quietly, "I shall let them have their monies worth Jack, so let's say two more rounds, eh?" They boxed hard for another ten minutes, and Scrapper seemed done in.

The Fifth Round.
Scrapper tried everything he knew to win the fight. The crowd roared and the fighters punched each other as hard as a kicking horse, Tom Pugh covered his face with a towel and said how could we meet the wager when all we had was but a few pounds. Then Mr Fosbrook took control of the fight. He turned Scrapper into a corner and punished him severely, with lefts and rights to his body and his head. Scrapper Bill sank to his knees and Fosbrook held back so that he might stand again, which he did. I was looking straight at David at this point and he winked his eye before setting again on poor Scrapper Bill. Boxing is a very violent sport as Scrapper will testify when finally his brains are unscrambled and he is able to talk. Mr Fosbrook knocked him out just before the end of the round. The crowd booed and Mr Temple emptied a bowl of water over the fallen pugilist before raising David Fosbrook's hand. A good days work, though not without pain. We made our way quickly to, "The Star and Garter." The money was still safe inside the barrel down the cellar. All was well with the world, or at least for us on this day in Bewdley. We feasted on ham and pickle with fresh bread and oranges afterwards. After brandy and a Bewdley pipe of tobacco, we gave thanks for victory and a most handsome profit.

Sunday 6th April
We three went to St. Anne's church and did endure the wrath of the Minister therein. He drew many immoral conclusions from yesterdays boxing bout - gambling was a sin, fighting for money worse, inciting public disorder an outrage and finally, we were guilty of undermining the moral fortitude of a Godly society by allowing a black man, an enslaved black man, to beat up a white man and thereby challenge the good order

of our beloved community. For good measure, the preacher considered it an appalling calamity that a black man might now be in possession of some of the bounty money bet against him by supporters of Scrapper Bill. Perhaps he considered Mr. Fosbrook may wish to buy his freedom and lord it around Bewdley as a freeman who had earned a place in the social order incompatible with his lowly "natural rank?"

We listened to the tirade and sang as hearty as the rest of the Christians in the congregation. At the end of the service, we went back to our lodgings for a good hearty luncheon of steak, followed by rhubarb pudding. After that, we took gentle exercise up and around the Sandy Bank as far as the Old Town Hall. One or two people even wished us well after Saturday's epic battle, presumably they were people who had not lost their gambling money on Scrapper Bill. We then drank at, "The Black Boy" Inn, nearby on Wyre Hill, how many others of Mr Fosbrook's race had likewise sampled such fare, I know not, but we three enjoyed ourselves and thought much of the irony of David Fosbrook's situation. I hardly need to mention that after the "Grand Battle" of yesterday in which the lout Scrapper Bill suffered ignominious defeat, no one attempted to throw Mr Fosbrook out of the hostelry.

Monday 7th April
We went about our work today as best we could, but Smout's warehouse was the centre of interest for many local people who came to see, "The Boxing Black." Smout himself remained aloof from the effect of either the celebrity or notoriety heaped upon our warrior by the Bewdley'ites, who sang his praises and cursed his name in equal measure.

Tuesday 8th April
Smout bade us to go with him to Kidderminster by horse and collect a consignment of woollen stuffs from the cottages around Church Street. The weavers there are kept in conditions of abject poverty, men, women and

children alike. Smout payed them off, but their depression played upon my conscience and I was glad to be gone from there. There is much industry in Kidderminster relating most to the carpet trade, but the people are poor and the majority of their housing merely rough hovels that barely keep the elements at bay.

Wednesday 9th April
We today received a most unwelcome visit from the Reverend Fygge into Smout's warehouse. He strictly forbade Mr Fosbrook from further attendance at church, and also lashed Tom Pugh and I for our part in the plot. I was singled out by Reverend Fygge as a threat to social order. Smout listened without a word, then when Fygge had finished his tirade and was about to leave, he turned and said,
- I wish you good day sir!
- Sir!, said the Man of God, I wish you good day sir, and trust you will take the proper course of action for God and your country!
Our own course of action would be to take a logical measure directed by common sense - we would transfer our loyalty to either the Baptists or the Quakers, though the Baptists sing better and are numerically stronger hereabouts.

Thursday 10th April
I have deposited 200 guineas with Mr Samuel Skey in his Bewdley Bank on Severnside. This prospect - one of financial well being - conjures up many interesting choices on our part. However, my conscience is very clear upon the first choice.

Friday 11th April
To this end, I have spoken with Smout concerning the whereabouts of Mr. Fosbrook's erstwhile captain from the trow. Smout condescended to send word to Bristol for the man to return to Bewdley straightaway.

Sunday 13th April

The Quakers shall be our new spiritual allies, though their singing leaves a lot to be desired. Yet they welcomed particularly David Fosbrook into their midst, so that Tom and I were exceedingly happy, both for him and for us. I could not help writing down the names of these good souls, yet pray they are not persecuted for my so doing:

Charity Peacock, Hanna Stockwood, Martha Munn, Sarah Newey, Mary Willis, Catherine Smith.

The gentlemen were named - Nathaniel Cooper, Obadiah Clare, William Seager, Goodyear Wildey, James Penn and Edmond Hornblower.

They are kindly and gentle folk all and surely worthy of being called Christians. Their church is exceedingly simple with no decorous ornaments and without either pulpit or pews. Chairs are provided and the Quakers have nought but a simple wooden cross placed near a window to which they turn to face now and again as they talk of Jesus Christ the Saviour and the vain glory of arrogant men and women. The Quakers are against the evil slave trade. Why is this Society of Friends then not the predominant religion in England? Why is the Reverend Fygge not stoned out of town for the abomination that he is?

Friday 18th April

Sweet, warm rain fell on Bewdley this day. Still no word from Mr. Fosbrook's captain in Bristol. Mr. Fosbrook goes about his work with a new confidence since the Prize Fight, not that he was timid before, far from it, he always had a strong, proud dignity - but now smiles more and is a happier man for the receipt of respect.

Sunday 20th April

Charity Peacock greeted me into the Quaker church which is set near the meadows off Lax Lane and Load Street. She is a delightful women, fully committed to her church and saving the souls of Bewdley folk.

Wednesday 23rd April
Word at last from Bristol. Mr Thomas Wooton, gentleman of Virginia, is set for London from his plantations of tobacco and slaves.

Friday 25th April
The Bewdley Brotherhood burned a trow from Worcester. The haulier had refused to pay a toll, so his cargo was sent to the bottom of the river Severn, into the arms of the goddess Sabrina. I hope the man and his crew escaped a simular fate.

Saturday 26th April
I met for some business with Mr Skey at his bank. He is an entrepreneur and merchant of the new school, his business seems to be the production of chemicals and the acquisition of profit.

Sunday 27th April
The day being a fine one, quite mild with even an hour or two's sunshine, our Quaker group held a brief service, then walked the town. Charity and the others were I think, looking out for pilgrims to their cause, but set me in mind rather of a Press Gang for this Majesty's Navy as we strode out along the Severnside.

Thursday 1st May
A May fair was held in Load Street and the people of Bewdley treated the day as a half-holiday. Dancers and even actors performed for the public, and there were many side shows for our entertainment, though the dentist stall did a good trade, and any pleasure taken from that act by the participants could only have been gained after many measures of brandy.

Monday 5th May
The Widow Haddock has been very attentive towards me of late, enquir-

ing after my health, giving me the best beef and generally letting the household know of her especial appreciation and consideration. Likewise, Molly Adams is here a lot to the displeasure of Elizabeth Haddock. Molly brings various items such as bed linen, the occasional pot or pan and other pieces of household equipment from her Mistress Perkins on Sandy Bank who is engaged in such provision for people in trade. But Molly's attention is towards me, and not to some old pot or pan. Her fondness incurs the wrath of Elizabeth and on the occasion of Molly's last visit, instead of a fine supper, I had my chops and potatoes taken from my place at table by The Widow for merely mentioning Molly's name. Her tongue is sharp as a knife and her eyes flash like lanterns in the night, such is Elizabeth's wrath. However, her true nature is both passionate and warm as I have discovered on several pleasant occasions.

Thursday 8th May
I dreampt again of my Black Lady - we were as one in a fine four poster, but unfortunately viewed by people of the town. Our embarrassment was short lived because our bed fell through the floor as the mob approached us to spoil any remaining privacy. Thereby I heard nought but shouts and rough words as we lay together on the bed even as it flew between the floors. I woke sharply, having fallen out of my true bed to find Mr. Fosbrook at the door laughing as he heard my shouts and viewed me rolling about beneath the blanket in some distress.
- I was dreaming my friend, said I.
- The way you were fighting, said he, perhaps it should be you who fights Scrapper Bill the next time?
- Oh no, I replied, my energy is needed for love, not boxing. It's the ladies I like to dance with my good friend, I would soon rather be cast adrift in the sea than to jig and turn about with that ugly brute Scrapper Bill.

Friday 9th May
'Tis strange though how The Black Lady haunts me, yet haunt me she does.

Sunday 11th May
Our Quaker friends invited Tom Pugh, David Fosbrook and I up to Tickenhill meadows for food, drink and pleasant enjoyment. The fare was excellent, being retrieved from a large basket and comprising of ale, chicken, bread, some fruit, various other meats and even tobacco was provided from this Bounty of Delight. They prayed under the open heaven, what good and generous people these are who welcome strangers such as we with open hearts and kind, thoughtful words and deeds.

Tuesday 13th May
Mr Smout bade me go with him to the Civic Rooms and carry a special carpet for decoration therein. He is quite boastful regarding his newly ordained civic standing as a Burgess, but I did not encourage him to puff up like a toad for fear of him exploding into the air.

Thursday 15th May
There is to be a meeting in the town on the subject of the proposed Brindley canal navigation. The Burgesses are organising the said event and it is set for Saturday.

Saturday 17th May
The meeting was held at noon outside the Civic Rooms in Load Street. The Bailiff was introduced by the Town Crier with his hand bell and verbal grovelling. The case against the navigation was put with the prejudice expected of small town politicians, ably assisted by The Rabble and The Mob of Bewdley Brothers, merchants, lackeys and general spoilers against everything their "betters" were against. Smout was forced to speak, which he did rather feebly, then others took up the cause with more vigour, particularly those involved in the river trade. Yet Samuel Skey, the master manufacturer, banker and merchant, remained cooly aloof and stayed silent. He is the craftiest of them all, for he knows well what is to come, yet refuses to commit himself for or against the project.

The bowyers, hauliers and trowmen are pathetic, not because of their trades, which are noble enough, but they refuse to acknowledge any other species of the earth or trade therein. If they had their way, bankers, locksmiths, blacksmiths, bakers, butchers and the whole host of, "competitors and non-boatmen," would be thrown into the river.

Me thinks 'tis time for change!

The Bailiff let the discourse run for nearly two hours, yet still no one dared speak for Brindley's canal navigation scheme to link Bewdley with the inland towns without a river. But what was evident to surely more than just I, was the quietness of the senior tradesmen and merchants. Fear of The Mob shut them up as tight as clams. A motion rejecting any attempt to cut the canal into Bewdley was put by The Bailiff to the assembly and carried with no dissenters.

Here endeth the first lesson.

And so, "The Loyal Motion from Bewdley" as it was called would be sent to The House of Commons and the various members from hereabouts, none of whom were in attendance. There is to be no mention of the most used term regarding the proposed canal, so the, "stinking ditch," will be referred to by its' proper dignified name, for the sake of, "civility and decorem towards the Noble Members." As the meeting was breaking up, I heard two coracle men talking together,

- It'll come boy, said one, mark my words, for there's more profit in canals than the river.

- Aye, said the other, and how about us poor folk, how will it be when the trade has gone?

Friday 23rd May

Our money still sits in Skey's Bank and The Mob has not burned him out as word says certain members of The Bewdley Brothers are keen to do, for Skey did not speak against, "The Stinking Ditch."

Saturday 24th May
A sense of calamity is in the air but amongst the lower classes only. The fear is all about the canal of course, but their mood is ugly and I shan't be drinking in, "The Mug House," or "The Saracen's Head."

Monday 26th May
A rough neck came to Smout's warehouse to seek me out. His name is John Metcalf and he has a prize fighter by the name of Jed Wilks. He proposed we should match our men for a wager of 300 guineas. I told him I would consider the issue.

Tuesday 27th May
David Fosbrook wishes to proceed with the match and so I agreed to meet Metcalf in, "The George," where we came to terms. Apparently his Mr Wilks is, "Champion of the North," and unbeaten after twenty events. Metcalf puts me in mind of a bull-baiter's terrier, all snarl and snap. An undesirable if ever I met one. The bout is set for two weeks from this Saturday, but this time will take place in the Meadows near Lax Lane.

Wednesday 28th May
Metcalf deposited 300 guinneas into Skey's Bank, so the match now is definitely on, I told Mr. Skey I proposed leaving our winnings on deposit still with him, after Mr Fosbrook had thrashed Jed Wilks. Skey laughed at my certainty but Metcalf stormed away like a scalded pig, just the reaction I had hoped for and anticipated.

Sunday 1st June
A glorious day to be alive. Our Quaker friends held their service, and we walked the town with them. Goodyear Wildey does not favour the Prize Fight yet does not condemn us. Charity Peacock wishes Mr Fosbrook well and hopes he comes to no real harm.

Tuesday 3rd June
As the day of the fight draws closer, I grow more nervous, not because we might lose our money, but for Mr Fosbrook's sake.

Friday 6th June
Smout's warehouse has taken on the appearance of a gambling den. Many people have come in to lay a bet on one fighter or the other, the money being about evenly placed on each. Smout is fortunately out of town, so we have a clear run at cashing in on our venture.

Monday 9th June
I have now seen Mr Jed Wilks Esq, and an ugly beast he is.

Tuesday 10th June
Smout has returned to the fold and seems quite pleased with himself after his business in Bristol. He is not so pleased with the trail of people coming to his warehouse to place bets.

Wednesday 11th June
I met Charity Peacock on Severnside. I mentioned my message for Mr. Thomas Wooton of Virginia had gone to Bristol some weeks ago. What Charity told me next caused great surprise. Mr Wooton is apparently from an old Bewdley family and left for Virginia as a young man. She had no idea what had become of him and was shocked by my disclosure.

Thursday 12th June
I have ensured that Mr Fosbrook has enjoyed the best of Widow Haddock's food over these past days. Also, I paid Smout 2 guinneas for my warrior to absent himself from the warehouse until after the fight. This evening, I went with him and Tom Pugh up into a hostelry near Kinlet to get away from the noisy clatter of Bewdley.

Friday 13th June
We came again to the inn and spent the night in peace and quiet to ensure good sleep and rest was had by all. I suspect Mr Metcalf would have hired louts to shout and stone, "The Star and Garter," thereby depriving my boxer of his deserved rest.

Saturday 14th June
We made our way back to Bewdley in a gentle rain beneath an ominously darkening sky. Elizabeth was happy to see us and cooked an early luncheon of steak, potatoes, cabbage, carrots, and parsnips. David Fosbrook and I then went to the Quaker's church, as previously arranged. We sat in silent prayer for some time before Charity and some of the other Friends bade us farewell and wished us luck. So in the rain we made our way down to the river side meadows, pushing our way through the crowd to reach the stage that had been built to allow proper view of the contest. Perhaps eight or nine hundred people, maybe more, were already at the ring side. Mr Fosbrook held his head high as Mr. Temple came towards us and shook our hands
- Wilks looks a vile bully, he said
- Sir, said I, bullies have to be put in their places, what?
- Indeed yes sir, he answered, though not too quickly, for the crowd's sake, eh?
Wilks was first into the ring and pranced around it like a dancing bear, holding his arms aloft and shouting to the crowd to gee them up. That he was indeed an ugly brute was apparent to even those at the back with little or no eye sight. His great bulk was carried on his menacing frame, the huge arms wore fists like horse hooves, shoulders as wide as a door frame, and the un natural, awful focus of all this awesomely gruesome flesh and bone was the man's face. Urgh! What a ugly, ugly face he had, a devilish, evil mocking look which defied natural explanation and humour. His nose, in proportion with the rest of him, sat like an alien mound of bone upon his lower temple, between cheeks as gnarled as bitten leather - the

chin seemed as a chisseled, yet moving lump of rock from which a beard of ivy or ferns or grass or moss or something awful had sproated. The man's ears had been battered and hung like slashed leather portraying a pair of awful curtains either side of his devilish dark deep set eyes. The merest thought of combat with Jed Wilks made my knees knock and my hands shake, but in the crowd, fervent and shouting at the tops of their voices, no one noticed I'm certain.

Then David Fosbrook entered the gladiatorial square, to jeers and cheers in equal part and I ducked under the ropes to be with him.

- What about him David?, I asked.

- We'll see what he's made of Jack, said he.

But I already knew the answer to that though I didn't let on

- pain, brute force, massive punishment to be inflicted by the brutes huge body, I thought. So I smiled through clenched teeth and gripped David's arm as a gesture of confidence and show.

Mr Temple stepped between us with his bell and tried desperately to shout some rules of combat above the row.

- No kicking, he said, no gouging of the eyes, no biting. I shall ring the bell after ten minutes.

- I shan't need ten minutes!, roared Jed Wilks, let me get at him!

Mr Temple realised he'd better start formally and very quickly, lest The Brute got at my man before he had a chance to clang his bell, so clang it he did, after the briefest introduction of each contestant.

Round One

God help David Fosbrook, I thought, as the boxers moved to face each other. But then I properly noticed the true size of my man also as they squared up. He was taller than his opponent and muscled as brilliantly as any man alive. Whereas Wilks was ugly, Mr Fosbrook stood as hand-some as a theatre player and was proud of his colour and his manhood. His good looks were unspoilt by fists, unlike Mr Wilks who must have taken thousands of punches to the head and face.

Wilks swung a huge arm at David, and missed by a mile, then tried to move in on him by taking plodding, heavy steps in his direction. But when Wilks moved forward, Fosbrook stepped quickly and neatly backwards or aside. The crowd booed. They wanted blood. Wilks chased Fosbrook around the ring, then just as Wilks was almost at a gallop, Fosbrook landed a superlative blow to his jaw and the ox was felled into a heap of staggering flesh and bone.

My God - the crowd went wild! They jeered and spat, then threw mud and turfs as the rain came down, demanding Wilks got up to face the Black Gladiator of Bewdley Town.
Mr Temple inspected the beached Naval Hulk.
- Are you fit sir?, he shouted.
- Fit for murder!, yelled Wilks as he scrambled to his feet unsteadily and as heavily as a bull at a closed gate.
The battle was joined again. As Wilks got back his senses, Fosbrook punched him quickly many times to the head for good measure. Wilks came forward, relentless and awesome still, yet Fosbrook stepped aside and punched his head again making Wilks fall into the ropes and lose himself. Metcalf shoved Wilks back up and cursed his man's performance. Metcalf was incredibly brave from outside the ring, and Wilks was brave inside it. He chased and punched the air for ten more minutes at least and I reminded Temple to ring the wretched bell, which he finally did to mixed applause.

- This rain will spoil the show, said David
- Are you hurt?, I asked him.
- No, he replied, and I thank God for it.
Round Two
Wilks took on a vile attitude, taunting Mr. Fosbrook, yelling at him to fight and saying he was a black devil who would not stand still. Nor would my man stand still - he danced, he skipped, he dashed back and forth, pop-

ping out a fist, left and right, as Wilks stalked his quarry. Now Wilks was getting cut around his eyes and the blood began to flow. My man saw this and hit him harder with sickening, thudding knuckle blows which cut deeper into the scarred flesh of Wilks who must have been in dreadful pain with each telling blow landing more efficiently than the last.

Wilks now stood in the middle of the ring, pawing the air without contact or real purpose. Like a Matador, Fosbrook stabbed him again and again - like a wounded bull, Wilks took each blow with anger then rage, unable to protect himself or fight back at the black boxer who clearly now was the better man. Metcalf yelled for action by Wilks, for more effort, for more fight. But the fight for Wilks was for his senses and wounded pride, so he stood, glued to the floor boards, swaying and throwing his fists at the air.

Mr Fosbrook then set about his adversary with efficiency and numbing violence. Left punches, right punches, straight and curled, up, across and down. More blows to Wilks head, more blood - groans from the crowd, despair from Metcalf, then merciful oblivion as David Fosbrook smashed Jed Wilks into unconscious submission.

Mr Temple stood over the victim and counted to five seconds, then ten before ringing the handbell to a crescendo of noise.

- I declare Mr Fosbrook the winner! he yelled, The new champion!

He raised his arm high into the air and Mr Fosbrook took applause, then just as quickly as he had danced around the ring, he knelt down to Wilks and cradled his head in his hands. Temple threw water onto both, but the rain already was drenching us all. Wilks was half dead and David Fosbrook was concerned enough to get whisky for him from Metcalf who didn't want to know, and scuttled away like a thief in the night.

And so it was left to David Fosbrook, Tom Pugh and I to carry poor Jed Wilks to a cart and set him in the direction of Stafford after my paying the carter a guinea to take him to Kidderminster. As for us, we were soon taking shelter from the torrential rain inside, "The Angel," to the general acclaim of all those who had been present at the Prize Fight. Perhaps some might consider the issue of a, "Bewdley Champion," to be worthy of support - perhaps even a certain Burgess and Merchant? I am sure those who see future advantage from association with the victor and his party will soon step forward.

Sunday 15th June
And as was proper, for David Fosbrook above all, we three again visited our Friends the Quakers for their Sunday service and gave thanks for victory and rude health.

Monday 16th June
As half expected, Smout welcomed us into the warehouse as conquering heroes, even suggesting if the weather was good, that Mr. Fosbrook should sit outside on a barrel, so the popuiation might be better aware of, "The Champion's" employer.
Smout paid for luncheon at, "The George" for Tom, myself and Mr Fosbrook. How ironic, but when our pennies were short, Mr. Smout gave us nothing except honest employment, yet now we have money in the Bank, he gives us luncheon! However, Smout can not give Mr Fosbrook his freedom, but maybe I can. I've squared it with Smout, (money into his hand), that Tom Pugh may go to London after Mr Thomas Wooton. My plan is thus - to get Wooton, the slave owner, here in Bewdley on the pretext one of his next of kin is dying and wishes to see the man from Virginia, who made his fortune, for a final time before she meets her maker. If that ploy fails to get the man here so I might get Mr Fosbrook his freedom, then indeed Mr Wooton does not have even a half of the common, human decency, society assumes he does have, though my assumption of his humanity is anyway pitifully bleak. So Tom set off in the coach for London and Mr Fosbrook went to the Quaker chapel to pray.

Tuesday 17th June
The Law hangs like a yoke around the neck of David Fosbrook. Certainly

he could flee anywhere in the known world, or the unknown come to that - the deepest parts of South America, Asia or Africa itself - yet, "British Justice," would bring him back to account as a slave. There is a madness which says a man can be enslaved - lawfully and forever - but he might yet enjoy Freedom and the other kind of, "Justice," ascribed to all free citizens - if he is able to buy out his Enslavement. Money is the Demon but the Liberator to! Though all money is made, spent, controlled and worshipped by men and women, and the Golden Throne it is put upon, is worshipped and covetted most, naturally, by the rich and powerful.

Wednesday 18th June
On such a beautiful day as this, how can slavery exist within our world? The sun is hot, though we enjoyed a shower of rain early on, but now, the population of Bewdley goes about its' work as if within a Paradise, blessed by the gods and the river Sabrina. But the night gave a different interpretation and a huge fight broke out in Welch Gate. Needless to say, the Brothers were at its' centre.

Thursday 19th June
Elizabeth Haddock is very attentive towards me and we made love in the gardens about here. See how a man is seduced by a pretty face and glorious sun and warm, fresh wind? Good food also does entice such amorous feeling, and kind words and most of all a smile which indicates love itself. Yet, I must not slip under this Lady's spell entirely, for I keep another sweet also - Molly is another love with wondrous gifts aplenty for a man such as me, who is young and able, without real care or anguish in such matters as are between my ladies and me. I try to detach myself a good piece away from the serious business of Mr Fosbrook's freedom, but even he encourages me towards my true nature that must be given some rein, else my head will explode and I shall have to become a celibate Monk or Priest and that would not suit me at all.

Friday 20th June
Celibacy played no part in my fancy today and I did'st woo sweet Molly Adams, her Mistress Perkins was away from the house on Sandy Bank, so Molly and me took our liberties in the bedchamber, uninterrupted except for the crowing of a red rooster outside in the yard. His song proclaimed his roosterness and I dids't proclaim mine, and my own sweet love for Molly, as the sun peeped 'oer the lavender-sweet sheets to look at my girl and the sun itself.

Saturday 21st June
As if all of this love making, were not enough to drench the most ardent of lovers such as I, I dreamed again of my Black Lady, whom I called out by her name - Lucy it seems, though I couldn't swear, for it was but another dream, though a good one indeed, as we were one, my Black Lady and me.

Sunday 22nd June
Perhaps I must yet become an Apostle of Celibate Worship? My women fill my head and it's time for Quaker chapel with Mr. Fosbrook.
As the ardour of the day is quenched as a candle is expired by a cover, I sit now at my desk in the rooms of, "The Star and Garter," and contemplate a few matters of late. The Quakers are like a rock which stands proud above the earth, though they would deny such an arrogant claim as that. Tom Pugh is still gone and I am mulling over the question of slavery once more.

Monday 23rd June
The Reverend Fygge was today spotted speaking with the Bewdley Brothers. 'Tis peculiar how the Godless stick together, what?

Friday 27th June
Many cattle today were driven through Bewdley, set o'er the bridge for

Kidderminster. The people hereabouts collected the dung for their garden plots, though Elizabeth allowed me to forego the dubious pleasure of collection.

Saturday 28th June
I met with Mr Skey, just to be sure my money (our money), was safe in his Bank, as of course it was. He wonders what I might yet achieve with it and I shall keep him wondering yet.

Tuesday 1st July
Another consignment of tobacco was delivered to Smout's. His premises were filled to the rafters with boxes and bundles of the leaves, the rest was quickly dispersed around the town to the shop keepers and publicans.

Wednesday 2nd July
A heavy rainstorm greeted the day and Bewdley was awash with water, so David Fosbrook and I sat inside Smout's warehouse, occasionally venturing outside for fresh air and to see the river.

Thursday 3rd July
There is a great deal of water now flowing within the Severn and the streams are too fast for the boating trade, so the Brothers sit, scowling, outside, "The Mug House," and, "The Saracen's Head," a pretty picture indeed to greet strangers to the town.

Friday 4th July
Tom Pugh is back from London with almost the worst possible news. Mr. Wooton had left London for America the day before Tom arrived to seek him out. However, Tom paid a man very well to ensure that word is sent to Bewdley in a few months time, because Mr. Wooton is set to return once more to London on business. I fear poor Elizabeth Wooton must linger at death's door for a good deal longer before her relative sits at her side for

comfort and a final farewell.

Mr. Fosbrook took the news very well, yet I did detect a sadness in his eyes, but he quickly gave a wide smile and said, "The Lord is with us my brothers, and I have faith in Him."

Sunday 6th July
I have confided in Charity Peacock of my intention to free David Fosbrook. She kissed my cheek and gave me a smile that was both wonderful and sincere. Charity told me I was not the rogue some claimed I was - I readily agreed and said how dare they, and we laughed together in her chapel after the others had gone outside.

Monday 7th July
There is further sickness in Kidderminster. This time the fever has taken hold amongst the carpet weavers. Several have died this last week.

Tuesday 8th July
Smout says the health of many poor workers in Kidderminster has worsened and a temporary hospital is opened near the mills.

Wednesday 9th July
Cholera not confirmed, but the fever is serious. The Quakers and others in Bewdley have gone to offer help.

Sunday 13th July
Hanna Stockwood, one of the Bewdley Quakers, was taken ill yesterday, surely because of her close contact with the sick? Goodyear Wildey led the prayers for her and all the others affected with the fever. I spoke with Charity at some length about the wretched pestilence and we agree. The fever is more likely to strike down the poor than the rich. I observed the same in London the year before last when many poor souls were taken. The reason seems simple enough, even to one not of the medical profes-

sion, if there is such a "profession," other than the one we currently "enjoy," perpetrated by the brigade of "amputate, leechify or lock in a dark room without food or water" - Quacks!

The poor are weaker and therefore prone to ailments, the poor are deprived of good food, their hovels are cold, draughty and let in the rain. They work all hours until exhausted - they fight each other and sap their strength. In short, the poor are usually scrawny and often sickly, therefore unable to fight off infection. The urban poor are worst affected, their rural brothers and sisters seem stronger and more fit to survive. And of course, once an epidemic takes hold in a built up area of housing, it spreads like wildfire because of the proximity of one person to another.

Monday 14th July
The turnpike on Bewdley bridge is closed to all travellers from Kidderminster.

Tuesday 15th July
Hundreds of cattle are held on Sturt Common, waiting to come through Bewdley. But with the fever at such a dangerous level in Kidderminster, there is confusion as to the sensibility of taking the cattle there, the animals would have to be kept at that town's market for some time and which farmers would dare venture into Kidderminster to purchase them?

Wednesday 16th July
It seems the issue of the cattle has been solved. Under the cover of darkness, a thousand head were crossed over the river near Lax Lane. By the time the Bridge Warden was wakened, the last few stragglers were being herded on to the Wribbenhall bank. The drovers were quickly away in the direction of Chaddesley. And so the drovers avoided the Bridge Toll and settled the argument about whether Kidderminster was a good bet for marketing cattle at this present time. Chaddesley is far enough from Kidderminster, about five miles, for farmers and buyers to feel relatively

safe away from the fever. Yet I think the Burgesses and Wardens of Bewdley will take measures to ensure such a daring escapade does not take place again. The loss of revenue is a serious business for such men and I've heard already that the Bewdley Brothers could be conscripted to defend the shores of the river and guide such, "unpatriotic and foreign villeins," through the Turnpike. Set a thief to catch a thief then?

Friday 18th July
Poor Hanna Stockwood died this morning. Her Quaker friends were with her and are extremely upset. Her funeral is set for Sunday and Hanna will be laid to rest in the little Quaker churchyard in Bewdley. David Fosbrook wept at her passing. What Jed Wilks failed to do therefore was achieved by the sweetest, kindest woman who cared for David as a brother. Wilks could not break him, but Hanna reduced the big man into an emotional, defenceless and distraught individual, unable for a time to defend himself or use his massive strength to fend off an adversary. Death came like a thunderbolt and floored Mr Fosbrook as it took poor Hanna Stockwood.

Sunday 20th July
At 2p.m., Hanna's coffin was borne into the Quaker cemetery, after the most beautiful and touching service I have ever witnessed. They all spoke - her Brothers and Sisters of her congregation. Obadiah Clare and James Penn were very upset and Martha Munn placed flowers upon the casket. Charity cried rivers of tears, but affirmed they were tears of joy for Hanna's life. I felt humble in such company and wept myself.

Monday 21st July
Further reflections on the issue of slavery - white people as well as black, are held in bondage. It is not that uncommon for a destitute pauper to sell himself to a landowner for work. I know this practice also results in the poor wretches being transported to the Americas to work on the plan-

tations. God knows how they fare! This practice is thought by some to be ended long ago in Medevil times, but it is not. So it is possible to see black and white men, women and children working in the fields, side by side, around the mansions of Virginia and, if the search is thorough enough, Worcestershire, Shropshire and elsewhere in England. High minded churchmen such as the Reverend Fygge, aristocrats and those with the vested interests of the property owing class, will deny the practice of slavery exists at all in England. But it does exist. The Workhouse of Kidderminster is filled with such sad, destitute and hopeless wretches willing to sell themselves to the highest bidder. Often, such people have incurred debt to landowners and farmers, so the money they receive as the ticket to slavery, goes straight back to the Master Slave Owner. The new rich and aristocrats who have made huge fortunes from slaves, sugar plantations, tobacco etc, have mansions in Worcestershire and throughout the land. They wrap themselves in a Religious - Christain - Holy - Godly cloak of immunity, then for good measure, imbibe deeply with a cleansing, guiltfree dose of legal immunity. Why is there no movement to stop such vile practices? I think only because the poor people are afraid.

Wednesday 23rd July
The Widow Haddock is on good form, cleaning her rooms, singing, going about as if she hadn't a care in the world. Her ale is good, as is the brandy and tobacco. Elizabeth therefore enjoys a healthy trade, though her business is less intense than similar inns and hotels in the town centre. Her customers are mainly very local to this part of town, but she does have travellers and the occasional trader or farmer staying for a few nights at a time. We cannoodled in the kitchen after breakfast. She was exceedingly generous and free with her love to me.

Thursday 24th July
The day is very warm, though a nice breeze comes off the Severn and, as always, it cooler on Cole's Quay, Severnside, near "The Mug House."

Could it be the Devil's Hand is always upon that corner of Bewdley? Trade is slack, mostly I fear because of the Kidderminster fever.

Friday 25th July
I was at the last of my paper yesterday. Today, I purchased fresh quantities and also ink from a local trader, Richard Bibb, who has a small printing house, a kind of factory with several men working there. He lost an arm as a coal miner in Highley and gave up the trade, he said, "before I lost the other." The quality of his printing is however good and I hope his business prospers.

Saturday 26th July
I called to see Molly Adams at her employer's residence. My status has risen at least a little because Mistress Perkins growled at me in a much softer tone than when I called before The Prize Fight. A nephew of hers, a Mr. Henry Longmore, was sat in the garden. The fellow is a captain of His Majesty's Worcestershire Militia. He displayed interest in the fight, but more interest, I thought, in Molly. However, Molly and I walked out towards Bliss Gate and the evening was warm and dry, altogether near perfect to enjoy our love in a field of barley corn. I took her home late and let myself in round the back of, "The Star and Garter," going quietly up the stairs to my bed.

Sunday 27th July
I lay in bed until Elizabeth brought breakfast up on a tray.
  - You're quite the Lord and Master, lying there in your
    Manhood, she said, as she gave me the plate of bacon,
    eggs and bread, now get up Jack Nowles, or I shall have
    to get in with you, she laughed.
Needless to say, I ate the breakfast and then Elizabeth got in with me. Oh
- the joys of love for a young man given his fancy. She stayed with me for
quite a time, talking, kissing me and paying me the rudest attention, in

the course of which I fell asleep, through my exertions of last evening with Molly, and again with Elizabeth. She finally left me and cursed me to get up. I did not until after 2.

Monday 28th July
Tom Pugh, David Fosbrook and I swam in the river. Smout had gone to, "The George," and said we could close the warehouse for an hour until he got back. His "hour" at, "The George," stretch often to two and even three, so we took a chance and played easy with time. We swam confidently to the Wribbenhall side down near Lax Lane then walked the bank for a few hundred yards to swim back over. A group of boat hauliers were pulling a trow, and I recognised them as belonging to the Bewdley Brotherhood. What an ugly crew, a surly mob of ignorant brutes. If the canal does come, may they be dispersed to the four winds, thereby allowing Bewdley to become altogether more genteel, refined and sophisticated, as Cheltenham, or Bath or Malvern. I jest, for Bewdley is a working town, but it would non the less be a better place without that gang of cut throats. One of the jokes told by Bewdley folk is, that officers of His Majesty's Navy are scared stiff of being Press Ganged into service with the Bewdley Brotherhood.
So after we'd rested for a while, we swam back over to the Bewdley side and leisurely took our time walking along Severnside South Quay to the warehouses and buildings of Bewdley. We had been back but for a moment or two and were sitting on barrels when Smout came up to us.
- You seem a little damp boys, he said
- Aye Mr Smout, said Tom Pugh, but none the worse for our swim in the river.
- Good God, said Smout, but I didn't realise I employed three fish. Best be careful boys or the fishermen here abouts might gather you up in their nets.
Mr Smout then, was quite a happy man after his time in, "The George Hotel." Least ways, he slept the rest of the afternoon on his chaise-lounge

as we made inventorys of the goods recently in.

Tuesday 29th July
Word is the fever in Kidderminster is no worse than it was, but the Bridge Turn Pike remains closed.

Wednesday 30th July
The Bewdley Burgesses met in the Civic Rooms to review the situation regarding the Brindley canal navigation. It seems their Member of Parliament would sooner enjoy the pleasures of London Town than take the Bewdley issue seriously. This report enraged the wretched Brotherhood, the members of which actually burned an effigy of Brindley in Load Street on this night.

Thursday 31st July
Mr Skey stands out like a peacock amongst some of the other merchants and traders. They know he has the real money (and some of mine, least I forget). Rumour says he has sent word to Brindley already inviting him in.

Friday 1st August
It appears that Captain Longmore is not alone on his visit to Bewdley, though he said nothing of his companions to me when we met. He is based near Heightington, some two miles from here in farm buildings with a score of militia men, troopers who spend time sharpening swords and cleaning muskets. The burning of Brindley's effigy seemingly caused some alarm and word has gone out from magistrates and others that Bewdley might need to be defended from its' own people.

Saturday 2nd August
The troopers came on horseback into Bewdley and trotted around the town as if out for a jolly jaunt. Small groups of people gathered here and

there to watch them. The mood was sombre, because everyone knows why they are here. I noticed though that the groups numbered less than 12 - fear of the Riot Act being read was therefore taken seriously. Could this be how the Bewdley Brethren are indeed to be dispersed to the four winds? Not by loss of employment because of Brindley's canal, but by having their heads, legs and arms cut off by Longmore's troopers and the pieces thrown into the river? We shall see during the next day or two whether or not the Brothers make a move.

Sunday 3rd August
A clever move by Captain Longmore, for he took his troopers into St. Anne's church. I was told their swords were placed near the alter, well away from the door and any possible thieving of their weapons behind the trooper's backs by people or persons unknown, people like the Bewdley Brethren, no doubt. The Reverend Fygge was most pleased to welcome the soldiers and urged them to put money into his offertory box. As for we three, we went again to be with the Quakers in their little chapel. Prayers were said for Hanna Stockwood and also for Mr. Fosbrook that he might be delivered from wicked enslavement.

Monday 4th August
Pressure is mounting for the bridge to be reopened, deputations of traders have petitioned the Burgesses and the magistrates. Yet things in Kidderminster have not improved, so it is doubtfull they will get their way.

Wednesday 6th August
Some of my Quaker friends have again visited the sick in Kidderminster. Edmond Hornblower and Obadiah Clare accompanied Catherine Smith and Charity Peacock to the temporary Hospital. Their report back was sorrowful indeed. Two men and a child died last week, but no further deaths have occurred since Sunday.

Thursday 7th August
The four Friends went again to Kidderminster, over Lax Lane crossing at night, taking good food for the sick and various medical herb remedies, and of course, the power of honest prayer.

Friday 8th August
The Friends are back. Things are a little better. No one is certain exactly what the fever is, but fever cases have been brought into the hospital and the weavers are continuing to ply their trade in their cottages and sheds, but in a mood of melancholy and grim acceptance of their fate.

Saturday 9th August
One or two traders have taken matters into their own hands, having paid off the bridge warden to turn a blind eye to their large carts which they took over the bridge last night. Everyone knows who the transgressors are, yet no penalty has been inflicted against them. I should mention that Smout is not such a bold fellow himself to have undertaken such a venture, so we remain quiet.

Saturday 10th August
Bewdley is a ghost town. Nothing moves, the people largely stay indoors and there has been just a glimpse or two of the troopers, walking quietly around the buildings.

Monday 11th August
More movement in the night, though of course, the carts were not brought down Welch Gate. The noise would be too great. The town woke again properly and the people go about their business.

Tuesday 12th August
It seems the bridge will indeed be reopened for Kidderminster, if no further deaths are reported. The need to trade is great, but the fear of death is

greater.

Wednesday 13th August
Smout received a consignment of Virginian tobacco. Much of it was
promised to Bewdley traders and they quickly took theirs, but Smout has
need of it for Kidderminster also, and he will wait to see if he is able to go
next week.

Thursday 14th August
I write this piece at night after everyone has retired to their rooms in "The
Star and Garter." It is very quiet in the streets, hardly a thing moves and
it is still very warm from the heat of the day even now, though cooling a
little. I think of my Black Lady in the candlelight, though of course, she is
not here. It is strange to be haunted such, and seduced by an apparition
that is yet more living woman than misty spirit. But Lucy quickly disap-
pears, deserts me for her special place where I may not reach her. And so
I think of Elizabeth and Molly, my women of real life and love. As I look
from my open window, I see a cat treading carefully across a wall in the
gardens, its' shape picked out by lanterns and lights from outbuildings
and stables over the background and towards, "The Horn and Trumpet."
How strange, this life, and my being here in Bewdley when all the world
calls me to it, each place, each country with its' people and customs and
strange alien tongues. Different Gods, but the same desire to live and love
in peace. But these desires seem so easily flaunted by the cannon and
sword, in ships and armies, to kill and destroy. And everywhere, calami-
ty and pestilence wait in the shadows to strike, as in Kidderminster where
the people live in fear for their lives.

Friday 15th August
I finally slept as the last piece of the night gave way to the dawn. I break-
fasted well with Tom and David and we set out for Smout's. There is an
expectation that the bridge gate will open soon. The hospital in

Kidderminster has been closed since yesterday, though I am unsure why. Have all the sick been thrown out, or cured, with no new cases?

Saturday 16th August
The bridge is open. Smout sent his tobacco across with a local team of drivers. There is much traffic again for Kidderminster. The Burgesses, with the magistrate present in Load Street, declared the crisis over. An old man shouted out, "A plague on all o' ye! Tis comin' o' pestilence for all the sins o' mankind. Ye fools t' think ye can cheat the Lord by takin souls to 'is bosom." He was led away by a trooper and cast into jail for disturbing the peace, but only held for an hour until the crowd had dispersed.

Sunday 17th August
It is quiet again today. We visited our Quaker friends and walked the riverside up to Arley, taking bread, ale and cheese. I returned alone to, "The Star and Garter," letting Tom and David go with Charity and the others to the riverside meadows. Elizabeth was alone in the sitting room, her boy having been taken for an outing by an Aunt.
- There you are Jack Nowles, she declared, I thought the devil had taken you off.
- We walked to Arley, I answered, you should have joined us.
- And who would look after the Inn?
- Anyway, how are you, Elizabeth? You seem a little uneasy.
- I'd like to know your intentions, she said seriously.
- Intentions? I countered, not yet knowing her true meaning.
- Are you going or staying?
- I'm staying, I replied, why do you ask?
- Because I am with child.
Her words hit me like a hammer. With child!
- No, I said, it can't be.
- It is. And you, Jack Nowles, are the father.
I staggered to a chair and sat down heavily.

- Lost your tongue?

- No, I answered quickly.

- Say something, then. Something nice.

- Err, you don't look pregnant.

*- Well I am!, she asserted, and around Christmas time, I shall give you a
son.*

- Err, you will?

- Yes I will, now come here and hold me you great fool of a man!

*As I prepare now for bed, the world seems still spinning around. I am to
be a father. The revelation demands my utmost attention. I must clear
my head. I should sleep and see how the morning finds me.*

Monday 18th August

*The day had not subsided the shock. At breakfast, my two friends talked
freely, but I kept my own counsel. Elizabeth was radiant and pleasant to
me. But further shock was to follow me that morning as we worked at
Smout's. Molly Adams asked to see me and Smout led her in.*

- Molly, I asked, how are you, my petal? You seem very happy today.

- I am, I am, she answered, and I can't wait to tell you.

- Tell me what, Molly?

- I am with child Jack, she sang as prettily as a bird in a tree.

*The import of her words knocked me over and I sat heavily on a sack of
rice.*

- With child?

*- Yes! she shrieked, isn't it wonderful Jack? I'm so happy.
When shall we be married?*

Tuesday 19th August

*I had to talk to someone and I spoke to Tom and David Fosbrook, quietly
and seriously at Smout's when he was at "The George."*

*- Hearty congratulations, Jack, said Tom, I always knew you to be a strong
contender for fatherhood. Yet with two women, each providing you with*

a child, things are not as straight forward as they might be, eh?

- Never a truer word, old friend, said I, how about you David? What do you think on the issue?

- Jack, I will stand by you into the Jaws of Death, and if you bid me, I should help you stand with your two ladies and their children when they are born.

- Thank you my friends, said I, for it seems that love making has sprung a trap on me that calls for very serious consideration. Whatever happens, I shall not desert my new families, though it will take a good time yet to decide how the matters of marriage, or household shall be settled.

- But time is of the essence, Jack said Tom, and the clock is ticking, loudly and quickly. The next few days passed as if time had taken a carriage ride around the town, galloping, racing, failing to heed serious matters of the world.

Monday 25th August

But it dumped me down hard on that Monday morning. Mr. Skey wanted me to invest my, our money, with him into business, and not let it remain safe in his Bank.

- Chemicals are the thing, Mr. Nowles, he said, and there's good profit in their production. Pewter can't be finished without chemicals, and there's other metals such as brass, iron and lead, and they all need treatment and I have the factory for it. Put your money with me and within the year, it will double in value.

He was persistent and genuine enough with his enthusiasm for the project and it was true his business was a success. But I refused to tell him what I wished to achieve with the 400 guineas and so I declined his offer.

Tuesday 26th August

So must I plan for two 'wives' and two children? Am I duty bound, honour bound, to cease all further dalliances, daring, exciting liaisons, in favour of sobriety and quiet rectitude? I think not, for I am young, but clearly decisions will need to be made, and shall be made in the fullness of time.

Wednesday 27th August
Gypsies have again come into town and settled in the meadows towards Dowle's Brook. They sing and dance in the streets, whilst their companions attempt to sell little goods and ornaments and collect money for the singing and the playing of their instruments. One man plays the violin as sweetly as the angels might. Where did he learn to play so beautifully? No academy has spoiled his natural gift, I'll wager, his ability is natural or God given as my Quaker friends would have it.
Molly came again to Smout's, filled with excitement still. How shall I tell her Elizabeth Haddock is in her same condition, yet filled, I think, with somewhat less innocent excitement? Elizabeth is more worldly wise than Molly, but am I less wise than either?

Thursday 28th August
Given silent tongues of David, Tom and I, it might yet be possible to prevent Molly and Elizabeth discovering the other is with child. Until that accusatory information is divulged, I can rest easy. If they discover the 'mutual truth' so be it, for it would take a malicious tongue further to attribute parenthood to me. But here I am, in a kind of 'peculiar state', of not knowing where my duties, or love, should lie. Elizabeth has done well not to blurt out her condition in front of Tom and David Fosbrook. And whilst she does not realise they know the truth, she keeps her secret from them. The same with Molly when she comes to see me at Smout's. There is no display or rough talk on her part, for which I am grateful, yet uneasy just the same.

Friday 29th August
Elizabeth says her baby is due in December, near to Christmas.

Saturday 30th August
Yoiks! Molly says the same.

Sunday 31st August
After such news, it was nice to enjoy the peace and quiet of the Quaker chapel with Charity, and the rest. Charity is exceedingly attractive - no - I musn't even contemplate such unworthy and lewd thoughts.

Monday 1st September
It is hot, the people go about slowly and there is much drinking in town, particularly down by the river. Trade is still slack, though the traffic continues to Kidderminster, but not like before.

Tuesday 2nd September
The troopers are billeted at, "The Boar's Head," on Dowle's Road, six at a time. Captain Longmore often stays with his Aunt on Sandy Bank. Mr. Smout says the troopers will soon be with drawn back up to the farms in Bliss Gate.

Wednesday 3rd September
All plans to withdraw the troopers must surely be squashed after last night's brawl outside, "The Mug House." The soldiers came off the worst, but only because of the overwhelming numbers of the Bewdley Bretheren. But what do the authorities expect when the militia is ordered to occupy a town against its will? It is as if the troopers were a foreign force of occupation, though truly small in numbers and as yet they haven't actually slaughtered people in the streets.

Thursday 4th September
Revenge was taken by the troops on the Bewdley Bretheren. A dozen or so of the militia returned to, "The Mug House," and proceeded to dish out beatings to those they recognised from the previous night and a few others

for good measure. By the time the Bretheren had sent runners for help, the damage was done, many heads were cracked and when sufficient numbers of Bretheren had gathered to have made a serious attempt at reversing the battle, the troopers drew swords and muskets to put them in their place.

Friday 5th September
"The Boar's Head," has many free rooms now because the soldiers have gone back to Bliss Gate, a less than dignified retreat, but they have resumed their patrols of the town and now are more fearsome than before to the local people, whether they belong to the Bretheren or not.

Saturday 6th September
The haughty and irreligious Reverend Fygge struts around town with a ridiculous air of ungodly pomp. The man is an ass. He yesterday denounced an old woman of being a witch and demanded her burning. Surely we have long since stopped practicing such barbaras cruelty, even here in Bewdley.

Sunday 7th September
The congregation at St. Anne's seemed geed up on their dispersement after the sermon by the Reverend Fygge. As they entered the streets from the church door, many had adopted a similar, haughty air to Fygge himself. I can only assume some new law has been made which further persecutes Catholics and the other minorities. Why else would the Fygge flock be so happy?

Monday 8th September
David Fosbrook goes about his work as if he was already a free man, not because of my promise to him, but because he already has more dignity than most men. Smout has allowed us further liberty lately, in short, he trusts us to work well for him, even when he is absent on business or plea-

sure. We shall not let let him and his business down.

Tuesday 9th September
Smout suggested I attend a meeting of the Bewdley Council, as a public observer, and this I did. I was one of only 3 such public observers, the whole thing seems almost to be couched in secrecy, at least, one is asked by personal invitation rather than public encouragement. However, the business was interesting, being mainly consistent of a review of trade hereabouts and civic issues of public safety. Naturally, the debate turned to the militia and also the Bewdley Brotherhood. It seemed to me, the Brotherhood have several advocates amongst the Burgesses, though I detected a number of the others resented the Brotherhood's ill effect upon the town. Then the issue of the Brindley canal navigation was intro-duced. No progress was reported from London. But the recent outbreak of fever in Kidderminster had adversely affected trade and many Burgesses were not happy with the situation. Progress stares them in the face and some avert their glaze into the darkest corners of Coles Quay. After the Council rose, its' members retired to, "The George Hotel," and I slipped away to the warehouse. Smout returned late in the afternoon and seemed relatively content.

Wednesday 10th September
Today was a golden day, the sun warmed everyone in Bewdley, the sky was blue and the birds were singing. As for the river Severn, it flows gen-tly and its' goddess Sabrina surveys all that is hers.

Thursday 11th September
How can I avoid the issue of my ladies any longer? Each grows heavier by the day, though they acquit themselves with elegant decorem, each in their different ways. Elizabeth goes about her business without fuss and my visits to Molly, with her occasional ones to me, indicate she is sensible to our situation.

I saw Molly buying bread and waited until she came out of the shop, walking with her up the Sandy Bank to Mistress Perkins. Once the impending birth is discovered or announced, Molly will be turned out. Mistress Perkins is another Christian.

Friday 12th September
There will be no throwing out of Elizabeth Haddock as she owns her own property lock, stock and barrel. If there is any throwing out to be done, I fear it might be me who is thrown when she discovers the expectant condition of Molly Adams.

Saturday 13th September
I actually saw Elizabeth Wooton this day in Bewdley. She was in the company of an older man, perhaps the brother of Thomas the slave owner. Miss Wooton is an elegant lady, who would no doubt play the part well of a wealthy member of the Wooton family, living as she does at their mansion in the countryside in nearby Trimpley. David Fosbrook was with me and he pointed her out, having seen her before and being told by Charity Peacock who she was. Miss Wooton and the man were collected by a carriage and four and made a handsome sight going over across the bridge back to their English Nirvana. I am still determined in my plan for David. When word comes that Wooton is in London, I shall send Tom Pugh to bring him back by any means, though the import of the strategy is to convince the man his niece is gravely ill and wishes to see him before she dies. Failure to move on his part might yet necessitate Tom hiring cut throats to bundle Mr. Wooton into a coach, bound and gagged, then driven up to Bewdley for a meeting with me when I shall offer him money to buy David Fosbrook's freedom. If the man refuses - we three might have to flee, with our money, to parts new, but I do not wish to do that, particularly because of Molly and Elizabeth.

Sunday 14th September
We three visited the Quakers at their chapel. After their religious service, we went with the Friends into the chapel gardens for bread, cheese, fruit and drink. It was then Charity and the others told us of their abiding concern for David's plight. Each one denounced the state of slavery, the laws which made it so and the people who perpetrated such evilness. Goodyear Wildey then announced, quietly and without fuss, the Bewdley Friends were to form, "The Bewdley Society for Abolition of Slavery." Goodyear spoke of their seriousness about the scheme. They would advocate abolition in the town next Sunday. More than that, they would use their influence to convince other Quakers in the country to take up the cause. When they considered the time was right, a petition would be got up for distribution within Bewdley and the County itself. These are good people, strong and reliable - true Friends indeed.

Monday 15th September
I have discovered the reason for the Reverend Fygge's pleasure - he is to have a substantial and costly Vicarage erected in the High Street, paid for, of course, by subscription and supplement from St. Anne's church funds. So the Bewdley public will pay to keep Fygge in luxury not fifty yards from The Workhouse! Meanwhile, the bloated toad hops around Bewdley ignoring completely any true social cry for help from the poor, though the 'gentleman' bends the knee very well towards the rich.

Tuesday 16th September
With a sad and ugly irony, I see a beggar standing near the workhouse, just a few yards from the site of the proposed new vicarage.

Wednesday 17th September
With consideration to Sunday's meeting, I have become slightly uneasy. The Friends will put the case against slavery fairly and squarely. But what of the response from the people of Bewdley? These are not radical people

and certainly have not had moral and progressive spiritual leadership from the Reverend Fygge, and therefore 'politics' has yet to reach the citizens.

Thursday 18th September
How sad today to see three Negroe men put ashore at Severnside South. They were collected by roughnecks with pistols and bundled into a cart. I asked where they were bound
- Cleobury Mortimer, said one overseer, but I'd as just as soon throw them in the river here and now.
- Who is your master? I asked.
- No man is my master, but Mr. Moss is the man who has paid for these.
And so they were gone, three slaves carted off to serve on the farms of Shropshire, without friends, advocates or the rights of but the lowest English criminal. Fortunately, David was otherwise engaged in work elsewhere for Mr. Smout, else I fear the roughnecks may have suffered cracked heads and a dip in the river. But we were not ready to unhook the Negroes, as if they were fish on a line, to set them safely once again into a calm millpond to go easily about their lives as we do. Such temporary freedom as might be achieved by us could surely be ended by search parties, men with dogs, to hunt them down and to drive them into man - traps before whipping them back into servitude or worse.

Friday 19th September
According to Charity Peacock, 'our cause' is supported by several notable worthies, but they will wait to see the out come of Sunday before making a move. At least we have the element of surprise on our side, as well as God, (according to the Quakers)
Bartholemew Smout senses something is afoot, but he does not know what it is.

Sunday 21st September

The day was fine, the sun warmed the town and a gentle breeze aired its' streets. Tom Pugh, David Fosbrook and I made our way down the Gate, after a hearty breakfast from Elizabeth whose mood remains good. When we got to the chapel, the Friends were waiting, deep in conversation. Goodyear Wildley would lead the assault upon the consciences of the people of Bewdley, but helped strongly by the other Friends who would stand shoulder to shoulder as he spoke. Their place of intervention into the, 'wicked order of things,' was to be outside, "The George Hotel," in Load Street. And so after the service we made our way down there. We numbered fourteen, two more than the number required before the Riot Act can be read for disturbance of the peace and worse. But our effort on this day was to end an evil and instead put in its' place an equality between men and women as to the nature of their freedom and civil rights before the law. There were some people already gathered in ones and two in Load Street and others spilling out of St. Anne's. Goodyear started up.

- Hear the word of the Lord, God made all men equal and did free his people from slavery. But today, slavery remains in our own country, perpetrated by those who have turned their faces away from God.

One or two souls turned to listen and others walked towards us as Goodyear continued.

- Join with us here today and affirm your detestation of slavery and its' vile trade. Slavery is un-Christain. We must demand an end to this abomination.

More people assembled as Goodyear persisted with confidence for his task. He continued in that same vein, given strength by us all. It was indeed a revelation to behold. Many people now gathered around to listen and those decanting from St. Anne's joined us. Finally, the Reverend Fygge came down and stood to listen as other Friends joined in the condemnation of slavery. The Reverend gentleman watched us like a hawk, but said nothing.

- But slavery is what the law permits, said one of the men who had been

amongst the first to stop and listen.

And all the time, that good, proud man David Fosbrook stood like an oak tree, proud and majestic, daring any one of the assembly to offer violence. The Reverend Fygge slinked away as more gathered near.

- If our country were but fully civilised, said Sarah Newey, we would live as brothers and sisters, and each would be free.

James Penn Spoke next

- We should demand an end to the slave trade. The Burgesses should be told how the people feel.

- We feel well enough about the issue, said a man in the crowd, and God is surely with us and not you.

- You should be ashamed to talk as you do with the black man here, an old lady cried out, he's got no rights to hear Christian people talking so against each other.

- But we should not be against each other, answered Mary Willis, God wants us to be as one and cast out evil.

- If that be so, said another, then cast out the black man and let us live in peace.

- There will be no real peace in slavery, said Charity, for slavery puts all in jeopardy.

I made one or two notes of the meeting, though more was said that I can remember. But we held the gathering for half an hour until Goodyear Wildey said we were to end it for then. He promised we would return on Sunday next and the meeting broke up. We three accompanied the Quakers back to their chapel and they held prayer.

Afterwards, we considered the effect of our activities in Load street. At least we were not stoned or shot, but perhaps this was merely because the populace was so shocked at the contents of our meeting they were glued to the pavement, unable to throw or shoot? Several of the onlookers had been in favour of what we were saying, several were against and most just stood and listened. David Fosbrook thanked us all, but Goodyear proclaimed our activities were nought less than our duty to God and our fel-

low men. Least ways, we were happy and that Sunday will stand out whatever happens later. We reaffirmed our commitment to repeat the exercise on Sunday next. I am so glad to be with such folk as these.

Wednesday 24th September
Another reported death by fever in Kidderminster, yet no one seems unduly concerned amongst the merchant class if Smout and the rest are anything to go by. Severnside Quay badly wants more trade, the river is low and not too good for traffic because the trows are difficult to sail when much of the river bottom is so visible, particularly downstream. A fifty or sixty tonne boat under sail or being pulled by the gruesome Bewdley Bretheren, needs adequate water and this summer has been too dry.

Thursday 25th September
My ladies are in rude health. Molly is eating huge quantities of cheese and fruit. We go for walks in our free time, though my free time is somewhat less than hers, because naturally I walk out with Elizabeth also.

Saturday 27th September
At least now I know the names of our, 'notable worthies,' who support our cause against slavery. They are John Sturges, another Quaker who is monied and leads a quiet lifestyle in, 'Summer House,' at Wribbenhall, and the Havergal family of, 'Winterdyne House,' on Red Hill. However, these good people are not due to join us on Sunday, but stand ready to help.

Sunday 28th September
After our Quaker meeting, the Friends went into Load Street and took up their position near to, "The George Hotel." Goodyear Wildey commenced his preaching on the evils of the slave trade and some people gathered to listen. A little after that, the congregation of St. Anne's began to spill out into the street, the bells were rung and the Reverend Fygge came within

yards of the assembly. I watched him call over a rough fellow who had been waiting in a doorway, they spoke very briefly then Fygge sent him on his way down the street. Goodyear had got the attention of all present, persisting with his theme of, "good Christians do not stand idly by when a wrong needs putting right." But then, a magistrate came out of the civic rooms and began to read loudly from a paper.

- In the name of His Majesty King George III, I name this an illegal and riotous assembly, unpermitted by the law and I order it to be dispersed with immediate effect, for it constitutes a threat to peace and public order. The Reverend Fygge, the lowest of God's creatures, had instigated the reading of the Riot Act against his fellow parishioners! The people were aghast and some broke away immediately, recognising the seriousness of the magistrate's words. But others seemed to ignore his words and bided Goodyear to go on with his sermon. But in the confusion and banter of all concerned, matters took a more serious turn. I heard horses hooves very close, then six scarlet troopers were on us and at us. I saw Captain Longmore and heard him cry out

- Get away from here! Go home! Go quickly and go now! Several people screamed out and shouted in panic. The troopers drew their swords and circled us. Our people ran through them in every direction, but the troopers stayed their ground and did not persue us. The street was cleared and as I looked back from the bridge, I saw the vile toad Fygge talking to Captain Longmore with hearty intent.

Monday 29th September
It is early morning now and the others have gone to their beds. I still can hardly believe what happened yesterday, but of course we might have suspected such a brutal end to our meeting. Yet that will not be the end, for after we were dispersed by Longmore's troopers we made our way back to the chapel with a few extra people who stuck with the Quakers and were led into their meeting place. The Friends vowed to carry on with their crusade, but the methods of advocacy would have to change, at least in

part.

They will pursue street speeches and the like, but numbers will have to be kept far below twelve, for fear of having the Riot Act read. But also our work might now have to take on an altogether more secret and covert nature. Such a pity, but what use would we be to the cause if we were cast in prison or worse?

Tuesday 30th September
Our Sunday sermon has caused much debate. The Burgesses, with one or two notable exceptions, are solidly against such activity. Smout though, urges caution only, so I've put him down for us because he has not condemned or dismissed us.

Wednesday 1st October
I was summoned to a meeting by Mr. Samuel Skey at his bank and went with Smout's blessing. His words were a revelation. He cautioned me against such, "Public displays," but only because of the certain consequences which would inevitably follow.
"Your friends wish to change the world, Mr. Nowles," he said, "and so do I. My factory is the way forward. Industrial progress, Mr. Nowles, that is the thing, for it will render slavery unnecessary."
"Not unless it is abolished first," I told him, "Slavery could exist in factories as in the fields."
"But, Mr Nowles he said again, "I fear you go at it too soon. When industrialisation is truly established, we shall want political democracy to go with it. Do you imagine for one moment that such a state of democratic affairs could be based on slavery?"
I told Mr. Skey that I truly didn't know the answer to his question, but I preferred my way of intervention rather than his, which seemed to indicate another hundred years of slavery before anything was achieved.
"I ask you again, Mr. Nowles," he said, "To put your money into my business."

I naturally declined, but thanked him heartily anyway for his kind offer and more importantly, his sensible consideration of what might be done to end slavery.

Saturday 4th October
I think we have settled on the best course of action for tomorrow. We shall leave the Quaker's chapel and set off in small groups of three and four into Load Street, but only one group will settle there to preach the sermon. The rest will break away into Severnside and the Lax Lane area. Our preaching will last an hour after which time the friends will withdraw to their church.

Sunday 5th October
I write near midnight. How naive we were to imagine our campaign would be permitted, even by groups of three and four. Even as we assembled in the Quaker chapel, troopers on horses drew up outside. Captain Longmore dismounted and came inside.
- You are ordered to stay exactly where you are, he said, hold your service here if you must, then disperse, each on his own, back to your houses.
- Brother, said Goodyear Wildey, this is our house and it is God's house, you are welcome to stay and pray with us for an end to slavery.
- I shall not stay Mr Wildey, Longmore answered, and I give you warning to act on my instructions.
Longmore withdrew and left us in a most agitated state, not knowing whether to obey or not. I urged we did, others argued to disobey, but finally we did agree to hold our service and go home. Troopers swords and muskets would be more than a match for unarmed Quakers, and of course, they would not instigate violence themselves. And so we dispersed, as ordered by Longmore, with our cause burning strongly in our hearts and heads, yet with the bitter taste of first defeat on our tongues.

Monday 6th October
After our work today, we were told that a meeting would take place at, 'Winterdyne House,' which concerned our "good cause," and so Tom Pugh, David Fosbrook and I duly attended for 8' O'clock. It was of course no surprise to be greeted by Goodyear Wildey and the rest of The Friends. Also present were our hosts, the Havergals and Mr Sturges from Wribbenhall. I was surprised to see Mr Richard Bibb, my printer friend, and several other people I had previously seen around Bewdley but had no cause to speak with. Sarah Newey led prayer, with particular love to the memory of Hannah Stockwood, so cruelly taken from us. Afterwards, we discussed what was to be done. Everyone was of the same conviction, matters would be pursued, yet not by meetings held in the street. The Quakers of Bewdley said their Friends in the county would similarly begin to "agitate" in a quite careful manner to begin with, but if confrontation was to occur, the Friends would not be deterred. Public notices would be printed, Mr Bibb quickly offered his services in this respect. Letters would be sent to certain people within the community, urging they support the good cause. Meetings would be held from time to time and all of those present undertook to advocate the cause to whom ever they might meet.
The reality of troopers being based just outside Bewdley, mitigated against any person suggesting we openly flout the Riot Act and risk injury, imprisonment, or death. Yet because of the magistrate's action in calling out the troopers, we have been drawn together and remain determined.

Tuesday 7th October
I called to see Mr Bibb in his premises and he has already type-set a hand bill for circulation, it having being written by Goodyear Wildey.

Wednesday 8th October
David Fosbrook talks to me of Virginia, how he regrets so much the dispersal of his family.

Thursday 9th October
I dreampt of my black lady, she was happy and singing in the woods with the foxes and the red deer.

Friday 10th October
Elizabeth Haddock seems very well and does not force me yet to decide upon our future. Molly Adams does press me, but still I decline to give her an undertaking one way or the other. I am excited with our situation.

Saturday 11th October
The river trade has picked up, yet is not back to how it was before the fever hit Kidderminster. The Burgesses are preoccupied with the prospect of Brindley's canal. At least the issue keeps them off the slavery question and the Quakers advocacy for abolition. The troopers still parade the town, obviously carrying out the orders of Longmore and his superiors.

Sunday 12th October
The Quakers held their church service, with four troopers watching from outside in the road. The military surely did not expect us to repeat last Sunday's exercise? We made our way out afterwards and quietly dispersed past the noses of the troopers who seemed disappointed we had chosen not to breach the Riot Act.

Monday 13th October
Late last night, several of us stuck hand bills on the posts and doors of Bewdley, carefully avoiding the troopers who seemed asleep as they stood around outside, "The George." In the cool light of the day on our way down to Smout's, we viewed the hand bills, though some had been removed.

Tuesday 14th October
A poor wretch was in the stocks today at the bottom of Load Street near the

bridge. He had been put there for absconding from the Work House. It was a truly pathetic sight. The man is not a criminal, merely an urban peasant without work or money. My inclination was to set him free, but the poor man was in no condition to run, so I gave him bread and a little ale, but had to leave him there. He was released during the evening to return in time for the Workhouse supper, a real banquet, I am told, of potatos, bread and tea. How considerate, to set him free for that?

Wednesday 15th October
Mr Bibb is in Bewdley gaol! His premises were raided in the early hours by, "the proper authorities," - magistrates officers, troopers etc. A large amount of damage was done by, "the proper authorities." Bibb's printing machines and plates were broken up and he was arrested.

Thursday 16th October
Bibb is in court today on a charge of disturbing the peace and printing information likely to cause disorder.

Friday 17th October
The Friends attended the court hearing, as I did, but David Fosbrook was advised by us to stay away, which he did. We found a friendly lawyer from Kidderminster, a Mr Donald Jones, who did the best he could for Bibb's defence, against the anger and hostility of the Court. No character witnesses were allowed and English, "Justice," was administered swiftly with indecent haste.
Bibb was fined £80 and sentenced to one month in gaol, to be served in Bewdley. He refused to name any confederates or accomplices and acquitted himself with honour.

Saturday 18th October
The Quakers and we three paid Bibb's fine and Goodyear Wildey and I visited him in prison, taking food and drink. It is an awful stone cage

they keep him in, a place not fit for animals, so very cold and dark.

Sunday 19th October
After the Quaker's church service, several of us again visited Richard Bibb. He is in good heart but thankful his sentence was one month and not a year. The Friends have undertaken to visit Richard every day and give him food and clothing when necessary.

Monday 20th October
And so, the weight and fierce power of the state in its' local form has been brought down upon our heads. It is the same for friendly societies of Working Men or Trade Unions as they are called. Groups of men in trades such as shoemakers, carpenters, weavers etc, are already trying to organise into political groups to protect their trades, apprentice-ships and wages. Yet to swear an oath of allegiance to such a body would be illegal, I am certain. So the "movement" is undercover, for fear of arrest and deportation.

Tuesday 21st October
Events have taken on such a serious tone, I have been preoccupied by them and quite unable to give Elizabeth and Molly proper attention. However, I hope to set matters right soon.

Wednesday 22nd October
Mr Smout is much concerned about the court case and issues pertaining to it. He thinks I might be next to be arrested.

Friday 24th October
Elizabeth has noticed Molly Adams has flown from her nest.

Saturday 25th October
Smout gave us the day off, so David Fosbrook, Tom Pugh and I rode out to

Kidderminster and visited St. Mary's church. Richard Baxter was its'
Priest during the Civil War period and was, from his writings and the
records, much concerned at the condition of the poor. Nothing has
changed in that respect, except there are a few more rich men and women
in their mansions. But Kidderminster has several hundred carpet looms,
some assembled with others in factory sheds mostly near the river Stour,
and also countless looms exist in the rough dwellings of the weavers. And
I know that where Bewdley merchants and traders on no account want
the canal navigation, here in Kidderminster the factory owners demand
the canal comes to town. The Workhouse has been there for forty years
being situated in Vicar Street.
I am not surprised that the fever took such a hold here.
The population stands at about four thousand. Lord Foley laid out new
streets comprising over two hundred houses, but there are hundreds more
so close together that an ill wind spreads disease like wildfire. The hous-
es are situated around several prominent streets namely, Worcester Street,
Mill Street, Orchard Street, Coventry Street, High Street, Church Street,
Black Star Street, the Horse Fair and the central Bull Ring. Pigsties are
everywhere throughout the alley ways and gardens. There are more
slaughter houses in one confined area than I have ever seen. The stench
is sickening. Near every property are open privies which rain turns into
cesspools. So fever and cholera visit this mass of humanity, striking down
the victims like so many skittles. Economics dictates that the weavers be
assembled in one urban area, tightly packed to receive the wools and
yarns, cottons and stuffs for carpets. The weaving sheds are gruesome,
dozens of workers being captured inside them. There are dye vats with
rainbow colours for the wool, the wooden looms are quite large and com-
plicated and worked by hand with many children servicing the process.
We were allowed into one such shed. I told the overseer I might make an
investment in his company, a lie of course, but we wished to see inside.
Kidderminster has many ale houses, but unlike Bewdley, the place seems
quieter and without the river Severn, altogether less interesting. It does

have the little river Stour, but it is filthy and used as a drain, with all the filth from the factories emptied into it and many of the inhabitants using the river to dump contents of their privies. On the civic and education side, there is a Grammer School named after King Charles 1st and Kidderminster borough is administered by the Baliff and Burgesses.

David Fosbrook considered the weaving sheds inhuman places and the men, women and children therein like white slaves locked inside against their will. He said they reminded him of the black slaves of Virginia on the plantations, and the weavers were even denied fresh air. If there are similarities, then may the weavers quickly organise into political societies and then help in the emancipation of the Negroes. David was shocked by their urban poverty, as Tom and I were. So much for Mr Samual Skey's method of economic and political emancipation and democratic progress. I think progressive men and women must consider these issues very carefully before deciding upon courses of action to achieve freedom for slaves, black and white. But action must be taken and in the end, the majority of English people must surely make their weight felt or suffer further degradation.

Our return to Bewdley was quite sombre, we stabled the horses and got into, "The Star and Garter," at around supper time.

Elizabeth, as ever, was pleased to see me, and I her. Her belly now is quite large and her affection towards me demands a response. I afterwards spent time in her bed chamber and gave her my love.

Sunday 26th October
The Friends visited Richard Bibb after the church service and said prayers for him through the gaol door.

Monday 27th October
Our man in London has sent word that Thomas Wooton is to arrive within the week, so I now wait for confirmation of that. But matters are not easy. There is the obvious opposition by magistrates and others, perhaps

against the precedent itself of having a freed slave within its' community. There are no such persons here as David Fosbrook. Yet I know other freed men and women do exist in London and elsewhere. But this place is different. My plan to bring Wooton here is fraught with danger and could blow up in my face. Speculation does not help. Yet I am concerned.

Tuesday 28th October
Mr Smout is away to Shrewsbury. I asked if he might look out for Molly Adams and offer my sincere good wishes to her.

Wednesday 29th October
Bewdley is quiet, the troopers have withdrawn to Bliss Gate and trade is slow. Herds of cattle were taken across the river again last night to the markets at Kidderminster and beyond. A group of charcoal burners came into town for provisions. They are extremely poor. I gave the head man five guinneas and said it was on account from Smout for past services rendered. He took the money and probably thought I was a fool, for there had not been services rendered which had not already been paid for.

Thursday 30th October
Smout has returned from Shrewsbury. He did meet Molly who was fine and well with child.

Friday 31st October
I visited Richard Bibb and gave him food. He asked how everyone was, David Fosbrook particularly. I said he was well, yet anxious as to how future events might turn. Because of Richard Bibb's condition and absolute loyalty, I explained to him my plan for David's freedom. He considered it a most splendid objective and offered his help, when released from prison. He was uncertain whether Mr Wooton would actually visit Bewdley, even for a sick niece, and if he did visit, might not he wish to sell

his property. I agreed the prognosis, but still reckoned my plan was worth pursuing. Richard asked also for a warm coat and so I gave him mine.

Saturday 1st November
I received another letter from London. Our man writes that Wooton arrived a few days ago, but does not know where he is staying and asked for more money to pursue him. The wretch is obviously a vagabond, but I sent another ten guinneas to him by coach from, "The George," set for Bristol and then London.

Sunday 2nd November
Many of the Quakers visited Richard Bibb throughout the day. Their church service was extremely uplifting and gave me strength, not by religious hectaring, but by kind words and love. In the evening we assembled again at, "Winterdyne House," with the friends of The Bewdley Society For Abolition of Slavery. I noticed a few more new faces, but was very surprised indeed at the arrival of Elizabeth Haddock. She sat near to me and was made welcome by The Friends.

Monday 3rd November
I was, and am, impressed by Elizabeth's fortitude. Her walk to Winterdyne last night was brave and most encouraging. She declared against slavery as strongly as anyone else present and seemed content as we walked home after the meeting. And so today, there is a new realisation that Elizabeth is both a good friend and strong advocate.

Tuesday 4th November
Molly's absence plays on my mind, but I await communication from her, if there is to be any. Yet because she is not here with me, my affection is naturally given freely to Elizabeth. But for all that, I am still unsure.

Wednesday 5th November
The first real frost last night. The gardens are touched by it and cobwebs and mist seem to be right up to the door. Smout received several trows, tobacco being the largest element but also rice and tea were delivered. The Bewdley Bretheren hauled the boats to Severn Quay and were paid off. They were arguing and cursing each other as one of their number had heard from Worcester that Brindley was in the area surveying the land.

Thursday 6th November
The Bewdley Burgesses met and decided upon a strategy to keep the canal out of Bewdley. Smout informed me that the issue was very simple - if local land owners refused to sell their land to Brindley, the canal could be kept away. Simple indeed! News from Lancashire indicates land owners are offered such huge amounts of money that the canal navigation going forward around Manchester is indeed wondrous and all consuming. The owners of small parcels of land are more than glad to be paid small fortunes and the large owners get a King's ransome!

Friday 7th November
The Bewdley Bretheren held a street meeting and demanded that every local landowner declares against the canal. They stormed into the civic rooms, which were empty, and nailed a proclamation on the door, threatening action against land owners who refused to give such an undertaking. The letter, anonymous, had its' mark made thus - "The Bewdley Faithfull." (Alas, but only to themselves and the past)

Saturday 8th November
The proclamation had immediate effect. Captain Longmore's troops are back in Bewdley.

Sunday 9th November
Elizabeth came with us for the Quaker's service and was very happy with

them for their kindness and sincerity. On our way from the chapel, with Elizabeth on my arm, we walked along the riverside past Smout's warehouse. The air was cold, but the sun shone through the roofs and chimneys of old Bewdley and the town looked as fair as any. Yet within those streets and alleys an anger was fermenting which seemed set to boil into violence. We walked down Coles Quay and the boat hauliers were in argument. Elizabeth said we should turn back, but Tom and David Fosbrook supported my determination to proceed. All was well because the Bretheren ducked into, "The Mug House," and made way for us, yet I could hear their shouting even as we walked into Dog Lane.

Monday 10th November
During last night, the drunken fools set fire to the warehouse of a merchant land owner who they considered likely to sell Brindley his land. The fire was put out just in time to save the building, but much of the contents of carpets and shoes were lost. Two of the Bretheren have fled with the troopers in pursuit some hours later. It is rumoured the Brothers have taken refuge in Wyre Forest, but for their sakes I hope that is not true because the militia men have dogs and it is said Captain Longmore enjoys the hunt.

Tuesday 11th November
The troopers parade through the streets and notices have been put up offering a reward of twenty pounds each for John Butler and James Cox who must answer charges of arson. The penalty could be death or transportation. If the wretches are indeed up in Wyre Forest then I hope for their sake they bury themselves deep beneath the highest oak and hibernate for the winter. It is said they were drunk and angry at the prospect of Brindley's canal, but I see the issue as rather one of a malaise affecting all boat hauliers who see doom in the new cuts of brackish water being opened in England.

Wednesday 12th November

Butler and Cox are not captured yet, but the troops still search the forest. Even the charcoal burners have disappeared into the very ground they live on. Their tents and shacks have been temporarily abandoned because one of the merchants sent a team out today for charcoal and wood but there was no sign of the forest people.

Thursday 13th November

Of course, the arsonist incident has completely distracted attention away from the Quakers and the issue of street meetings and our posters against slavery. God moves in mysterious ways.

Friday 14th November

I visited Richard Bibb and gave him food. He is determined to repair his printing presses or if that proves impossible, to buy new equipment. Printing is now in his blood, but he will alas have to be restrained by his friends not to print posters against slavery, at least for some time yet.

Saturday 15th November

Mr Samuel Skey sent word for me to visit him at his bank, which I did. He was concerned about the current unrest, claiming it to be bad for business. He is a clever man. When the canal navigation comes to Bewdley or a place nearby to link the river with Kidderminster, Stafford and elsewhere, Skey says the Bewdley Bretheren will naturally obtain work on the narrow boats. However, the Brothers will no longer be able to exact an illegal tax from users of the canal. The river trade will also be transformed by the canal and so the Brothers influence will subside and be surpressed by new owners of boats and property. Skey's chemical works is thriving with his production of salt-peter, chemicals, even gun powder and the refining of gold. The gentleman wishes naturally for this state of affairs to continue. The nub of his argument therefore was to suggest that at the appropriate time, after the land deal is signed to bring Brindley's canal to Bewdley, Skey might provide a contract to the Bewdley Bretheren to supply their labour for the canal as well as the river Severn. But that situation is still some way off and his purpose in sharing ideas with me was to consider my measured, and apparently respected, response. Skey thinks I am a, "man of the world," and well qualified to judge. I said the scheme sounded fine, but I was unsure as to whether the Bewdley Brothers were capable of change. Skey insists they will be, when the time comes. He considers them to be the, "voice and conscience of old Bewdley," and the future of his chemical works and his bank depends upon the Bewdley people going along with his business ventures and giving his businesses their latent and overt support. Mr Skey is a politician without a seat.

There is an element of trust between Mr Skey and I. He thought my arrangement of the two prize fights was unsurpassed as a spectacle, but had been very risky. He heartily approved of the spectacle and the risk. Skey even talked of the Wooton family in our conversation, but I did not mention Wooton's ownership of David Fosbrook or my plan to free him. I merely encouraged Skey gently to tell me more about Wooton to gain his true feelings of the man. Skey does not like Wooton. Perhaps his dislike could even prove useful in the days to come?

Sunday 16th November

The hunt for Butler and Cox goes on, but they are not found yet. The rest of the Bewdley Bretheren tried to assemble near the civic rooms but the troopers broke it up. The Quakers service was well attended and Elizabeth was again present. Richard Bibb shall be released from prison tomorrow and The Friends will be there to greet him.

We left the chapel to find two soldiers just across the street, no doubt there to intimidate us. Goodyear Wildey wished them well, but they were not impressed by his genuine Christian warmth. On our way past St. Anne's, we saw the Reverend Fygge in conversation with parishioners leaving church. I swear I saw him turn into a horned toad and back again in the few steps it took to walk past him. It is cold today and Elizabeth has a good fire. There is ample wood from Wyre Forest and some coal we have stored in the gardens for winter. Elizabeth's hired hands are making ale in the out houses and so there is activity outside in the yards. Why is there no further word from London and how is sweet Molly Adams?

Monday 17th November
Richard Bibb was freed at midday to warm applause and hearty welcome from our Quaker Friends. The Havergals had provided a luncheon for Richard at Winterdyne and Tom, David and I took time off from Smout's to join the festivities. There were speeches, serious and jolly, in favour of the ex-prisoner. David Fosbrook offered his sincere thanks for what Richard and all the Friends had done for him. The luncheon seemed to continue until around five o'clock when everyone left in good spirits.

Tuesday 18th November
I called on Richard Bibb at his printing shop to find him working hard at repairing his broken machinery. He explained some parts were ruined but could be replaced and he had ordered them already. Other parts could indeed be mended and Richard was busily engaged in this. Elizabeth's lad Peter was helping out and seemed happy to do so having finished his schooling for the day with old Mr Blount the retired grammar school teacher. The boy says Mr Blount might achieve a place for him at grammar school, but not yet.

Wednesday 19th November
Mr Smout asked David, Tom and I to go up into Wyre Forest with a cart for charcoal. This we did and set out very early. It was cold, though dry. Deep in the woods, the fallen leaves were piled high like hedges in places driven by the wind into mounds six feet deep. Yet there was no wind today, the air was as still as the most sheltered spot in a town garden. All the time I had the feeling we were being watched.
We pushed on deeper into the forest, there was no songbird and the place

had a sadness I have not before experienced. David Fosbrook began to sing a hymn and Tom joined him. I thought I saw a movement in some thick bushes but only for a moment. As we drew near the place we knew the charcoal burners to be in, I heard a twig crack underfoot almost as loud a pistol shot, yet again, no one was visible. We approached a shack but I could sense no one was within it.

- It looks like the birds have flown, said Tom
- The nest is empty, said David, looking inside
- How strange that the charcoal burners and Butler and Cox have vanished into thin air, I added, but look, there is the pile of charcoal, so let's load it to the waggon.

This we did, and all the time, the eyes of Wyre Forest were upon us, a feeling we all had, though no burner or fugitive from the law was visible. With the charcoal loaded, we made our way from the shack. There is a beauty about this place that is time less. The forest has its' own existence, its' own time, life is within its' trees and ferns and everywhere the magic of a secret part of man's nature, a pagan refuge from other men with their houses and streets and hostile machinery. It was dark when we got back to Bewdley. We left the cart in Smout's yard, stabled the horses then returned to the, "Star and Garter" for a much needed, hot meal from Elizabeth.

Thursday 20th November
Longmore is in town again. I do not like the man, for he revels in the town's unrest and takes pleasure from parading about as if the Militia were an occupying army in a foreign land.

Friday 21st November
Blast and damnation! My man in London says Mr Thomas Wooton has left for Liverpool with him in pursuit. I now must wait for further news of my quarry, if indeed there is to be any.

Saturday 22nd November
Smout tells me he has been approached by a Burgess to openly declare for Brindley's canal. Smout will not, for he is a prudent gentlemen prepared to let others pave the way before declaring even that today is Saturday.

Sunday 23rd November
A mad wretch was put in the stocks on this day for abusing the King, calling him a pig with a crown. After the Quaker service, I saw him, still bellowing obscenities, and being pelted with rotten cabbages by several true Christians fresh from church. Ah! The English at play - what fun they have!

Monday 24th November
The gentleman had been released by this morning, freed presumably to insult the King in the privacy of his own hovel. Personally, I did not believe him to be a threat to the Monarch or the King's Peace.

Tuesday 25th November
Mr Blount called to see Elizabeth. He has secured a place at the Grammar School for Peter to begin in January. Everyone is happy at the news, especially the boy himself and Elizabeth is delighted.

Wednesday 26th November
Several of the Bewdley Bretheren were beaten up by Longmore's troops last night, having strayed down one dark alley too many, filled with ale and bravado. The troops returned victorious to, "The Boar's Head" and we heard them bragging and shouting throughout the night, no doubt getting more drunk with each hour that passed.

Thursday 27th November
A letter from Molly. She writes that she will stay a while longer in Shrewsbury and that she misses me a great deal. Yet there is something

strange about even these words, though they are written thoughtfully and clearly, ending with expressions of love.

Friday 28th November
There is much trade on the river just now. Many loads of vegetables, corn, barley and potatoes still go down river to Bristol and there have been large shipments of furniture, coal, carpets and pewter with brass and iron pieces.

Saturday 29th November
More tobacco, rice and cotton arrived on Severnside, some for Smout and the rest for the other merchants. We worked hard to unload it all and Smout treated us afterwards to dinner at, "The George Hotel."

Sunday 30th November
Our Quaker service was a long one and we had sensible debate in the chapel concerning slavery and the two fugitives from justice. Again, our party went to Winterdyne where the Havergal family did us proud with a feast far too good for King George III.

Monday 1st December
Our man has sent word from Liverpool, naturally asking for money to go direct to him at an inn called, "The Sailors Arms." I have therefore for-warded ten guinneas for him by coach from, "The George," this morning.

Tuesday 2nd December
Three more black slaves, two men and a young woman, were set down on Severnside today. David Fosbrook saw them and offered a prayer. They were from Africa, petrified and cold, dressed in rags and hungry. We fed and clothed them properly at Smout's before a team of four men from Ludlow came to collect them. A more pitiable sight I have never seen. They are to be put to work in a planters country mansion deep in the

Shropshire countryside. I felt angry and hostile to the the men who took them away. These black people were as different to David as I am from the illiterate charcoal burners of the forest. They said not a word as they stood at the Quayside, save, for a few in their own mother tongue, presumably to thank us for the food and clothing. David could run Smout's business and is the equal of any man. Those poor wretches will, I fear, never achieve equality amongst even members of their own race. God only knows where they lived, prior to their capture and transportation to England. Bewdley would surely have seemed a frightening place indeed, with its' boats and river people and the cold air that bites the skin. Yet they were the strongest, for many die in the boats and even before, their spirits and souls refuse to acknowledge their enslavement and the vile, evil chains and metal neck collars, and they simply die.

Wednesday 3rd December
They have caught Butler and Cox in the forest. Longmore went back for a third time with his dogs and fetched them out of a bunker beneath the leaves and ferns. The men were tied behind horses and dragged back to Bewdley, then thrown into its' awful gaol. A dozen armed troopers are placed outside to prevent an attempt at liberating the men. The Bretheren are woeful and the people of the town very jumpy as Longmore's troops appear on every corner. A senior magistrate is expected soon to try them. Butler and Cox will be lucky to survive the sentence. Their capture has brought matters to a head, so the people wait for the King's Justice to be meeted out to two misguided fools.

Thursday 4th December
Our river trade continues, but Smout is depressed about the arsonists capture, fearing civil unrest and more burning. Mr Skey also thinks the matter very serious indeed and warned me from taking any action at all which might be conscrued as being favourable to the prisoners, because the expected magistrate is not a man who takes interference with his jus-

tice at all lightly.

Friday 5th December
Today is my birthday anniversary, my twenty sixth. Hardly a day to cele-brate here in Bewdley, alas. The magistrate has arrived and the trial will be held tomorrow. Elizabeth has given me a pocket watch inscribed with love from herself and Peter. I kissed her and thanked her for her generous gift and saw a look in her eyes which was loving and kind. Elizabeth real-ly is a good woman, and I hope to God she is delivered of her baby safely. It is arranged that Doctor Peplow will attend her. As each day passes, I am more aware that a decision is imminent on my part.

Saturday 6th December
I write this entry knowing the worst fate awaits Butler and Cox. The mag-istrate was surplanted by Judge Slater, a man with a ferocious reputation. A Mr Fitzpatrick was employed at extremely short notice to legally repre-sent Butler and Cox. They pleaded not guilty to the charge of arson and endangering life and claimed they had been in the forest since the day before the fire. The court room was full and guarded by over three dozen troops. The prosecutor put the case strongly. There was no jury, because the Judge declared that the Riot Act having been read in Bewdley put the matter outside civil law and into military. It seems that Bewdley, to the knowledge of no single person, not even a Burgess or a rich merchant, realised the town had been under marshal law. Fitzpatrick did his best to defend the undefendable. The verdict was delivered in a peremptory manner by Slater - guilty of course, but Fitzpatrick was on his feet imme-diately to plead for clemancy, to no avail. Judge Slater sentenced Butler and Cox to death by hanging and ordered them to be taken back to prison after which the sentence would be carried out on Sunday. The people were left in a state of shock as the men were led away, shouting obsceni-ties at Slater and the soldiers and cursing the name of Brindley even as the jail door was slammed shut. Execution is scheduled for 8 o'clock in

the meadows by the river and a scaffold is being erected by Longmore's troopers.

Sunday 7th December
I was woken in the early hours and given the news by Tom Pugh who had ventured out into Welch Gate to discover what was causing the tremendous row. The word went round the streets like wildfire, even at five in the morning in darkness as black as pitch. Butler and Cox had escaped! During our Quaker's service in mid morning, it was said that everyone in Bewdley knew what had happened. A diversion had been created by a mob yelling for blood near the jail. They had taken Judge Slater prisoner and were parading him up to the very gates, threatening to kill him unless Butler and Cox were freed. The men wore hoods and could not be recognised. As the soldiers approached the mob, someone let the prisoners out with the only key to fit the lock. A hunting horn was blown and Slater was thrown to the ground. The hooded men vanished into the night and it is said that Butler and Cox were taken down river by boat. The soldiers caught no one in this episode and the Judge has ordered Longmore be confided to quarters to face military tribunal.

Monday 8th December
Bewdley is in a state of unrest. The militia are searching every property in the town for Butler and Cox who are no doubt well on their way to Bristol by now. Troopers are causing damage to business premises and domestic alike, and make it clear they consider everyone under suspicion and confederates in the break out. A sargeant Bowman leads the way, kicking down every door that remains unopened after two or three blows from his rifle butt. Judge Slater has called a special meeting with Burgesses, Smout being in attendance. He read them a different kind of Riot Act
- This is the most unlawful and dangerous town I have ever
  entered! You Burgesses preside over a seditious and god less mob!

etcetera, etcetera.

Smout seemed quite taken aback by the man's venom and was, if any-thing, slightly more sympathetic towards the stupid Butler and Cox than before the Judge came to our town.

Tuesday 9th December

Many members of the Bewdley Bretheren have been arrested and ques-tioned about the escape of Butler and Cox. The men swore on oath they were at home in bed when the break out took place. The lawyer Fitzpatrick is working hard to get them freed. There are after all, no wit-nesses who can identify the masked liberators and Judge Slater himself can hardly ignore these facts by pretending that he can, unless he wants the whole town to go up in flames.

Wednesday 10th December

In all of this uncertainty and local mayhem, I dreampt of my Black Lady. She appeared from a burning building, then turned to face the inferno and the flames were vanquished.

Thursday 11th December

A letter from Bristol. Wooton is there, and not now in Liverpool, and so I have written back saying his niece is dangerously ill and close to death. I signed it with my own name on behalf of the family.

Friday 12th December

I have confessed my plan to Smout. My reasoning for so doing was two fold. Firstly, if the plan goes wrong and Wooton hands me over to the law for false representation, Smout will find out any way. But also we may have to flee Bewdley even if Wooton does not set the law on me, but mere-ly refuses to sell David Fosbrook. In any event, Smout has been good to us and has a right to know. He might also yet be able to help.

Saturday 13th December
I called Doctor Peplow to Elizabeth and he stayed with her most of the day, but her baby is not yet ready for this world. David Fosbrook is the largest and kindest nurse I have ever seen, tending to Elizabeth with devotion and true Christian care.

Sunday 14th December
Ever true friends, the Quakers came to the, "Star and Garter," and held their Sunday service here for Elizabeth. We sang and prayed for peace and love in this world. Charity Peacock will stay with Elizabeth now.

Monday 15th December
Heavy rain for more than a day The river has risen quite alarmingly, trade is therefore difficult with a few trows coming up. Rumour has it that Butler and Cox did indeed make it down to Bristol and enlisted in His Majesty's Navy aboard a ship bound for the West Indies. Judge Slater still skulks around Bewdley with Captain Longmore who was finally restored to active service. It seems the Judge was enticed from his bed chamber by a woman of the night and then captured by the hooded men. The Judge therefore prefers the truth of even a military Tribunal not to come out and so Longmore was reinstated.

Tuesday 16th December
The rain still pours down upon Bewdley, the streets and alleys are awash with water, and 'tis difficult to tell where roads end and the river begins. All work on Severnside has stopped, so we sit waiting in Smout's warehouse, idly passing our time playing cards and smoking Bewdley pipes of tobacco. Tom went to see a game cock fight at the back of, "The Angel," and lost three guineas on a bird. No word then yet from sweet Molly Adams. It is peculiar to think that she and Elizabeth are so near to delivery and yet Molly, for all I know, could be already a mother or the Gods might have wrought down their wrath upon that sweet girl.

Wednesday 17th December
Charity Peacock has been a blessing for Elizabeth. She comforts her and cares for her as a sister or mother would. The rain has eased off, but the river is high and no trade is possible for the ferocity of the water.

Thursday 18th December
Bewdley is flooded. Sabrina, the goddess of the river Severn, is at its' very gates and a powerful thing she is indeed to behold. Today was without even a glimpse of clear sky, so dull and overcast without any natural light. And now a fog has fallen over the town so that day and night seem as one. No word about Wooton, but I have had a man near, "The George," for a week at a guinea a day, waiting for his coach. He is to tell me immediately upon Wooton's arrival, for a twenty guinea bounty.

Friday 19th December
Disaster! Wooton has vanished. My man in Bristol has written to me saying the gentleman has disappeared from the face of the earth, but he will keep searching. How can it be that a man of Wooton's prominence suddenly becomes invisible, even in a city as large as Bristol?

Saturday 20th December
Tom Pugh has left by coach for Bristol. If any man is able to bring Wooton to Bewdley, it is Tom.

Sunday 21st December
Again, the Quakers come for their service to, "The Star and Garter." We afterwards enjoyed a hearty luncheon of chops, potatoes and carrots, all cooked and served by the Quaker women who made David Fosbrook and I feel honoured by their prescence. Elizabeth was able to join us and I stayed with her well into the night.

Monday 22nd December
It is very cold today and snow has fallen. There is an icy wind which cuts through a body, especially down by the river. Smout retired early to, "The George," and David and I also finished just after 3. The world has closed in around Bewdley. At times like these I appreciate how it was in London, where the streets do not suffer flooding and it always seems that life is there. But here, the people have retreated deep into their burrows and the town has stopped moving. I do not like it. To make matters worse, the prospect of what might happen when, or if, Wooton gets here has cast a shadow over me. Elizabeth is entitled to my company, which I gladly concur, yet Molly beckons from the very river itself, for the fifty or so miles of wild, freezing water would take me directly to her in Shrewsbury. And so the elements conspire and work their winter misery against poor mortals such as we.

Tuesday 23rd December
I stayed awake throughout the night, talking and lying with Elizabeth. Charity Peacock finally ordered me to my own bed as the cocks were crowing. Today I shall face the world, even this closed, dark world of Bewdley, as a man who has decided his future. I am near to deciding and am now certain in my mind my choice shall be honourable, logical and extremely satisfactory.

Wednesday 24th December
I rose early and went to see Goodyear Wildey and explained my plan to him. My intention caused him pleasure. I returned to the, "Star and Garter," to wait for the Friends and to be with Elizabeth. I shall be sorry that Tom Pugh is not here, but David is like a brother, as is Tom, and so with my other true friends the Quakers, our new lives shall begin.
I went straight to Elizabeth.
- Where have you been Jack Nowles?, she asked
- To see Goodyear Wildey, I replied

- Hold my hand, she said, I feel my time is very close.

I looked into her lovely eyes and kissed her. She squeezed my hand with a strength I did not expect.

- I want you to be my wife Elizabeth

- Good God above! How can we be married when my baby is almost with us? If you want a wife, then you must wait, she told me.

- We need not wait, I said

- And how about Molly Adams? She has a call on you my lad or do you deny it?

- No, I don't deny it, I said, but I have decided whatever else ensues, I want us to be together. Will you marry me Elizabeth my darling?

- Yes,yes,yes, yes! But how and when Jack Nowles, that's the question and where's your answer?

- Goodyear Wildey will marry us here in this bedroom. The Quakers are downstairs, I hear them coming.

- Fetch them up! Fetch them up!, she cried, and hurry about it Jack Nowles for you have a way of leaving things until the moment has almost passed! I scrambled down the stairs. They were all there, Charity, Martha Munn, Obadiah, James Penn and the rest. They crowded into the bedroom as best they could, but one or two could only look in through the open door. Goodyear stepped forward, bible in hand, and I knelt next to Elizabeth who had young Peter on her left side, smiling and happy for his dear, dear mother. Goodyear began

- My dear friends, we are gathered here to witness the coming together in marriage of Jack Nowles and Elizabeth Haddock. Are there any who have objection, and if this be so, please speak now or forever hold your peace. Good! I thoroughly approve of the silence! Then in the sight of the Lord our Saviour, and with the authority given to me by the congregation here assembled, I shall conduct a ceremony of marriage between Jack and Elizabeth. Do you, Jack Nowles, bachelor of Bewdley, take this woman, Elizabeth as your lawful wedded wife?

- I do, I answered with pleasure.
- And do you, Elizabeth Haddock, widow of Bewdley, take
  this man Jack as your lawful wedded husband?
- I do, she replied
- I do as well, Peter added to some merriment from the assembly.
- You may put the ring on her finger, (which I did) and I now
  pronounce you man and wife. You may kiss your wife
- Thank you Goodyear, I gasped, and kissed Elizabeth for all I was worth.
- Three cheers for Elizabeth and Jack, shouted David Fosbrook, and thank
  God for them both!
There was much jollity and hymns were sung which rang out across the
roofs of Welch Gate
- Oh Jack, said my new wife, I am so happy, but I think everyone except
  Charity should leave. Fetch Dr. Peplow, for I think our baby is ready for
  this world.
The people quickly left, but David and I stayed in the next bedroom.
Elizabeth's labours continued throughout the day and then the night. Dr.
Peplow called me several times for brandy, boiling water and even for
food. David slept on a chair and I, the chaise-lounge. Soon after six in
the morning, we were woken by Elizabeth's cries. I went to her and with-
in just a few more minutes she was delivered of a beautiful baby boy.
- Here's your son Jack, Elizabeth said, a baby son for Christmas!

Christmas day 1762
Now mother and child sleep. I have told everyone the news - my Quaker
friends, Smout and even Samual Skey. I am exhilarated, overjoyed and
exhausted. I can scarcely believe that I am a husband and father, all in
a day. My head spins and I can't stop peeping in to Elizabeth's bed chamber to look at our son.
Charirty is with Elizabeth, and Dr. Peplow called in again to see her and
my son. He needs a name, our little boy, I must speak to Elizabeth and
decide quickly.

James! We shall name our son James. He will be Christened on Sunday at the Quaker's chapel here in Bewdley.

Friday 26th December
I have moved into Elizabeth's bedchamber, as befits a good husband. I am very content with the world this day. David and I went down to Smouts' warehouse, trade is very slack, the river is still high and the weather is cold. No sign yet of Tom Pugh, with or without Wooton. The trowmen and boat hauliers - the Bewdley Bretheren - have no work, so stand around idly on Cole's Quay and Severnside, between that is, their frequent visits to the riverside ale houses. A few troopers remain in town being lodged still at, "The Boar's Head." Richard Bibb called into Smout's and we had a good, honest talk. He is as anxious as I am about Wooton's arrival and will watch out for the coach.

Saturday 27th December
Snow fell during the night. Tom Pugh's journey was surely extremely difficult. He has been gone a week today. With luck, he should have got to Bristol by Monday or Tuesday at the latest, but the weather has been so bad that the trackways and roads might be impassable. Bartholemew Smout came home with me to see James and Elizabeth. He pressed a silver sovereign into his tiny hand, then gave it to Elizabeth, saying his having money on his second day would bring him and us goodluck. David Fosbrook has held James for the first time and he seems so small in the big man's arms.

Sunday 28th December
I hired a covered carriage for Elizabeth, James and I to take us to the chapel. She is naturally incapacitated, but managed the short journey in good spirits. We saw the bloated horned toad, the Reverend Fygge waiting outside St. Anne's church, no doubt thinking to himself of all the money that will come his way for the new Vicarage in High Street. James was

Christened by Goodyear Wildey and the Friends were in excellent spirits. We are going to start a, "Grand Petetion," against slavery both within the British Isles and throughout its' dominions.

Monday 29th December
The Quakers have decided we shall begin to sign the "Grand Petition," today on Bewdley bridge. Goodyear Wildey will declare in its' favour. Our congregation will certainly number more than that legally permissable under the Riot Act. And so, in the snow on the old bridge, we gathered, some twenty in number, to begin our struggle against slavery. David Fosbrook was of course with us and to my surprise we were joined by Barthlemew Smout. Goodyear Wildey led the way with a fine speech against the slave trade. To my utmost delight, our number was further increased by the presence of Mr Samual Skey and several other merchants of the town. Some members of the Bewdley Bretheren were below the bridge on Severnside, but came no further. Goodyear asked that I be the first to sign the Petition and this I did, quickly followed by all the others present, including Smout and Skey. Several troopers drew nearer to our assembly, but did not come onto the bridge. They watched our activity and Longmore no doubt recognised Samuel Skey and the others, so took no action. There was a feeling of pride in what we were doing. As we descended from the bridge down into Load Street, I noticed the Bristol coach making its way into town. It drew up outside, "The George Hotel," and I urged David to go with me to meet it. I had a deep feeling that this coach and its' passengers would be of vital importance to us all. Immediately Tom Pugh jumped out and called to me
- Jack Nowles! Here is Mr Wooton come to see his sister. What do you say to him?
Poor Tom must have been in a state of acute apprehension for all the hours of his journey, indeed longer, for his lie was cast down before that wretched coach journey was indeed commenced. But at last, here was the man at the centre of our intrigue, the one who could solve the problem

nearest to everyone or just as soon dash our hopes. The Quakers gath-
ered quickly, being eager to see Mr Wooton who then got down from the
coach to face us.
- Mr Wooton, I said, welcome to Bewdley.
- Sir, said he, I already know Bewdley, how is my niece?
  Are you the doctor?
- I am not the doctor sir
- Then take me to my niece
- But there is no need sir, for she is well and in good health
- Good health indeed! I am pleased to hear it, for this scoundrel Pugh
assured me in Bristol that the poor girl was dying, dying Mr Nowles. What
do you say to that?
The crowd pressed forward, eager to listen, as Wooton stared into each
face. And then he recognised David Fosbrook.
- Wait a minute! That man is David Fosbrook
- That is correct sir, I concurred, and he is the reason I have brought you
  here. You hold him in slavery and I wish to buy his freedom
- Sir! You interfere in matters that are of no concern to you
- That is not so Mr Wooton, I declared, for David Fosbrook is of concern to
  our community of Quakers and we want him freed.
Goodyear Wildey stepped forward and spoke as a true friend
- We will pay any price sir, he said, so please name it and let us take Mr
  Fosbrook into our community as a free man. He is a Christian, and as
  such, must not be kept in bondage
- The law of the land allows it, said Wooton
- But man's law is not God's law, said Goodyear, and is a far inferior
  thing
- And if you are a true Christian gentleman, said Charity, you will let him
  go
- Thomas Wooton, called Mr Skey, it seems these good people wish to do
  business with you. Will you disappoint them?
- Ah! Samuel Skey - I wondered if you might be a part of this.

- I am part of nothing Thomas, he replied, except the business community, and as such, I see slavery as an impediment to business and sooner or later, it will be stopped. So name your price, sir!

Silence fell over the assembly as the coach was taken to the back of, "The George." Troopers still stood near the bridge, but did not threaten us.

- I shall be free sir, said David Fosbrook, you are not a wicked man, but slavery is wicked. My family was sold in Virginia, I have not seen my sisters and brothers since we were children. I shall be free.

Wooton said nothing, but considered the issue with a severe countenance and held his tongue

- Name your price for this man's liberty, I asked, speak sir for we all await your decision.

Still he said nothing and contemplated further and longer so that he seemed struck dumb.

- Come along Mr Wooton, said Smout, we all await your decision. As for myself I must tell you that Mr Fosbrook has worked well in my warehouse. An excellent fellow, as strong as a horse. He could probably throw you into the river with one arm only, such is his physical prowess - oh please do not take that as an implied threat Mr Wooton, I merely mean't to say - well, there it is!

- If it were to be known that I was willing to give away my slaves for nothing, Wooton said finally, I should be bankrupt in one month, without workers or business associates. You people might wish this man to be free, but in Virginia and Carolina our system is based upon the plantations being worked by such people as he. One slave here or there, sold at a mutually acceptable price, will make not the slightest difference to the world. This being so, I am willing to sell David Fosbrook to you for, let's say fifty guinneas.

When these words were said, the loudest cheer of the year went up over Bewdley, hats were thrown in the air and several people stepped forward to slap Wooton's back

- Well done sir, said Goodyear Wildey, that Christian act will stand you in

good stead with our Lord God at your time of judgement

- Thank you Mr Wooton, said Smout, what a day this has turned out to be? The Quakers insisted that I take their guinneas and other coinage, even Skey and Smout put into the hat which I then gave to Wooton.

- Sir, you may keep your hat, he told me, I will merely take your money

- Spoken like a true man of business, said Skey, now let me please provide you with my carriage so that you may indeed visit your dear niece and her family.

And so, Skey and Wooton departed for Trimpley in the snow. We were so happy, David Fosbrook was at last a free man, as his spirit had always been. I thanked Tom Pugh with handshakes and bear hugs in delirious excess. We retired, arm in arm with David Fosbrook, back to, "The Star and Garter." Elizabeth was dumb founded and complete with joy and poor David Fosbrook cried like our new born baby, as I did myself. There would be no need to take flight from Bewdley, we were now the equals of each other in the eyes of the law, but a law that is still unjust and wicked. The last few days have been momentus ones indeed and still this year is not out yet!

Tuesday 30th December
We held a special service of Thanksgiving at the Quaker chapel. David gave a speech that was the most Christian I have ever heard, and surely its like must never have been witnessed in Bewdley or elsewhere? In the late evening, I walked alone down to the bridge. There was some ice in the still water puddles of the river bank, just like when I arrived one year ago tomorrow. I looked off the bridge and saw the Bewdley Bretheren in two's and threes, waiting for work, going in and out of the ale houses, arguing and swearing, exactly as before. But the world has changed.

Wednesday 31st December
To my utmost surprise, David Fosbrook bid me to go with him up the Sandy

Bank to Mistress Perkins. I could not believe my eyes, for there in a chair near the log fire was Molly Adams. And in her arms, Molly had her baby. I struggled to see the mite wrapped in blankets and woolens as tightly as the threads on a bobbin. But then, even in the poor half light of the cottage, I saw that the baby could never have been mine

- Look Jack, she said, I have a son the same as you and Elizabeth have your son

- He is my son, said David, but tell me you are not angry, tell me we are still friends?

I looked at that beautiful child and kissed his little hand. He was not African nor English, but a beautiful coffee colour with a face as sweet as an angel's, with Molly's good looks and David Fosbrook's deep dark eyes

- We are friends forever David, I said, and Molly and Elizabeth and our new little souls shall grow together as a family, with Peter as the little one's big brother. We shall be happy and make lives here as free men and women, and attempt to live in peace and fight for justice and freedom for all men and women!

This year of my life, 1762, thus ends as I write in my own bed chamber next to Elizabeth, with James in his crib and the fire giving warmth and light with the candle for my paper and pen and ink that has allowed me to convey most of what happened to us all, here in Bewdley by the river Severn in the county of Worcestershire, in England with its King and its' paupers, its' merchants and its' free men. And now I shall sleep, to wake with, the The New Year.

"Sic transit gloria mundi."